McLaren
HONDA TURBO

A TECHNICAL APPRAISAL

McLaren
HONDA TURBO

A TECHNICAL APPRAISAL

IAN BAMSEY

Foulis

Haynes
®

A **FOULIS** MOTORING BOOK

First published 1990

© RACECAR ENGINEERING

Published and Printed in England by:
Haynes Publishing Group
Sparkford, Near Yeovil, Somerset BA22 7JJ.
England

© Haynes Publications inc.
861 Lawrence Drive, Newbury Park,
California, 91320, USA

Produced for GT Foulis & Co. Ltd. by
RACECAR ENGINEERING
(Racecar Engineering Specialist Publications)
Editorial Director: Ian Bamsey
Research Assistant: Alan Lis

British Library Cataloguing in Publication
Data
Bamsey, Ian
McLaren - Honda Turbo - a technical
appraisal.
1. Racing cars
I. Title
629.228

ISBN 0-85429-840-1

Library of Congress Catalog
Card number McLaren 90-80310

Typesetting & Artwork by:
Photosetting, Yeovil, Somerset

CONTENTS

INTRODUCTION

When McLaren International asked Honda the chance of a significantly lower engine for 1988 the Japanese manufacturer unrolled a set of drawings saying, 'like this, you mean?'

The winning package was on its way.

Ahead of the engine layout McLaren Technical Director Gordon Murray sketched the cockpit of his illfated Brabham BT55 with its radically laid back driving position. It was a perfect fit. Better still, the mandatory reduction in fuel tank size from 195 to a meagre 150 litres meant there was no problem accommodating everything properly within an extremely low fuselage. The low line concept kept the centre of gravity low and significantly enhanced airflow to the rear wing. Aerodynamic efficiency took a leap forward and that was crucial given the tight race fuel ration.

The winning package was well on its way.

McLaren ditched a chassis structure carefully honed since 1981 to make the maximum of the potential of the low engine. In addition to a brand new monocoque it produced a brand new three rather than two shaft transmission to beneficially step up the drive from a lower-set clutch centre. Aside from bringing the crankshaft down, the way to the reduction in engine height was a shortening of the inlet tracts as Honda tuned for a higher peak power speed. That was necessary in the face of a major cut in boost while the strangled fuel allocation called for major attention to engine efficiency.

A winning package demanded more than aerodynamic efficiency.

Inevitably Honda's recipe included a significantly higher compression ratio. Of course, Ferrari took the same route and it was in terms of detail development that the Honda V6 shone through. For example, lower boost made atomisation of the toluene-based fuel on which turbocharged Formula One engines thrived more difficult. Honda overcame the problem prior to the start of the season. Ferrari still floundered. Honda achieved significantly higher fuel efficiency than its turbocharged rivals. And it extracted the race power to murder fuel free 3.5 litre atmo rivals.

A winning package was ready.

The amazing 15 out of 16 race wins of the 1988 Honda-McLaren turbo was truly success down to an overall package, as the humiliating failure of the contemporary Honda-Lotus turbo underlined. Lotus did not produce a low line fuselage, nor a bespoke transmission. Instead it angled its powertrain upwards, increasing the frontal area of the engine and lifting the centre of gravity of it together with that of the transaxle. Clearly, road holding and aerodynamic efficiency suffered. Meanwhile, the impressive McLaren International team showed how to wring every last ounce of potential out of the '88 Honda offering, which was a very special animal indeed.

Packaging to win.

A very special engine in a very special chassis, in this case an Anglo-Japanese combination devised, built and run by exceptional engineers and proven by equally talented drivers. This purely technical study can but hope to do justice to all the players - together Honda and McLaren International employed around 300 dedicated personnel. One, Ayrton Senna, deservedly won the accolade of World Champion. 299 worked just as hard.

Aiming to provide a rounded technical picture, the book commences with a look at the origins of the turbocharged Formula One car. Those who are

familiar with other works covering that same topic by the author will find this material familiar and may prefer to skip straight to the 'Background' section. While previous books by the author have covered much of the ground there, important new information has come to light in the research for this offering, including enlightening material provided by Honda.

Surprisingly, having been the most secretive manufacturer throughout the turbo era Honda subsequently released fully comprehensive engine information. That and the equally forthcoming attitude of McLaren International has allowed this book to probe the innermost secrets of the most successful Grand Prix car of the rear-engine era, the quite remarkable RA-168-E-MP4/4 of 1988.

Acknowledgements

This book would not have been possible without the generous co-operation of members of the Honda F1 Grand Prix Racing Team and staff of McLaren International. Honda Formula One Chief Engineer and Project Leader Osamu Goto took the trouble to shed light on many aspects of the RA-168-E and its higher boost predecessors while the SAE paper on the subject that he prepared with colleagues (SAE Technical Paper Series 890877) was a very valuable source of reference. Murray likewise provided full co-operation while McLaren Team Co-ordinator Jo Ramirez and Race Engineer Tim Wright filled in many details. Further, Ramirez helped compile and authenticated the Chassis Log.

Thanks are also due to Honda Formula One PR Eric Silbermann and his colleagues. The author referred throughout to the comprehensive documentation of the sporting side of the '88 Formula One story provided by Motoring News, Autosport, Autocourse, Sport Auto and Autosprint. Finally, acknowledgement is due to Racecar Engineering contributor Ingegnere Enrico Benzing who provided the important technical insight into the Ferrari side of the confrontation.

ORIGINS

Turbocharging is a form of supercharging, which is the process of forcing mixture into the cylinders of an internal combustion engine at higher than atmospheric pressure. For an engine of given displacement power can be increased by either increasing the amount of work done on the pistons or by raising the speed at which the engine operates. The easiest way to increase the work done on the pistons is to increase the weight of the charge. More fuel can be introduced almost at will but to increase power there must be a corresponding increase of air to allow full combustion. Pressurising the charge air prior to intake increases its density and thus the amount that can be crammed into the cylinder per cycle.

Unlike a supercharger, a turbocharger has no mechanical drive connection with the engine. It is a device that couples an exhaust driven turbine to a centrifugal air compressor by a short shaft. The idea is that the turbine harnesses the waste energy of the exhaust to drive the compressor which in turn crams more air into the engine. Correctly, this process is known as turbo-supercharging. Compared with supercharging, turbo-supercharging has the advantage of using waste energy in the exhaust pipe rather than engine power to drive the compressor, which boosts power since in effect it improves an engine's capacity to accept air. Harnessing the waste energy in the exhaust pipe to drive the compressor offers higher thermal and mechanical efficiency.

The turbocharger as pioneered by Renault for Formula One employs a single stage radial flow centrifugal compressor to provide the air pressurisation. This is linked by a short shaft running an inboard bearing system to a conventional single stage radial flow gas turbine. The turbine creates a flow restriction in the exhaust system so exhaust manifold back pressure increases. However, provided sufficient exhaust energy is converted into compressor work for charge air delivery pressure to equal or exceed pressure at the turbine inlet the engine's breathing should not be adversely affected.

The inlet manifold is under pressure and this will help push the pistons down on the intake stroke as surely as back pressure hinders the exhaust stroke. Back pressure is only a problem in so far as it can hinder the entry of a fresh charge into a cylinder. However, if an engine breathes well and charge air pressure at least equals pressure at the turbine inlet there should be no problem getting the exhaust gas out and a fresh high density charge in.

Running with a positive pressure relationship the turbocharged engine is able to exploit the potential of very dense charge air assuming, of course, the density increase is matched by additional fuel. However, it should be noted that the density increase will not necessarily match the degree of pressurisation imparted by the compressor since raising the pressure of a gas increases its temperature as well as its density. Any temperature rise is at the expense of density, and will cause higher internal engine temperatures.

The heating effect is clearly unwelcome and the actual pressure felt in the inlet manifold is what counts and this is often measured as gauge boost pressure - the amount added to the normal intake manifold pressure. Normally aspirated engine manifold pressure is typically just a whisker below the 1.0 bar measure of atmospheric pressure at sea level, pressure falling with altitude. An alternative measure of intake manifold pressure is absolute pressure - the total pressure felt in the manifold. Unless otherwise indicated figures quoted hereafter are for absolute pressure.

A conventional turbine impeller is of high temperature steel welded to a shaft to form the rotor assembly. The turbine has to withstand exhaust temperatures of up to 900 degrees centigrade and typically runs within a cast iron housing. Spinning at up to 90,000r.p.m., the shaft revolves in plain bearings fed with engine lubrication oil. The compressor impeller is of aluminium alloy clamped to the shaft by an end nut. It spins in an aluminium housing which incorporates the volute (a carefully shaped outer housing). The impeller blades accelerate the incoming air so as to impart a high velocity to it by centrifugal force, then the air is diffused into the volute, reducing its velocity and thus building up pressure.

It should be noted that compressor action is essentially aerodynamic: the turbocharger is not a positive displacement device trapping air in sealed chambers before it is compressed. Consequently, as engine speed and load increase its

aerodynamic qualities are severely tested. Critically important is the relationship between airflow and pressure. If flow is too low for the pressure build up in a system the air can stall and change direction - the phenomenon of 'surge' which can occur violently, causing serious damage. At the other end of the spectrum is flow that is disproportionately high for the pressure build up. Air flow can go supersonic at the inlet, which is inefficient and causes dangerous charge heating. If flow is too high there will be excessive impeller speed for a given pressure delivery, and it is possible to overspeed the impeller, causing it to burst.

Clearly it is desirable to run a compressor as closely as possible to its peak efficiency at all times. Running a compressor below its peak efficiency implies a greater power requirement for a given pressure rise. Low efficiency causes a disproportionate temperature rise. A compressor's overall efficiency - its adiabatic (effectively its 'pumping') efficiency - is reflected in the temperature rise it creates. 100% efficiency is a pure adiabatic condition with no heat entering or leaving the system but in practice some temperature rise is inevitable and around 75% efficiency is the best that can be achieved. Further, the turbocharger typically has to serve an engine operating over a wide range of speed (r.p.m.) and load (throttle opening).

Different turbochargers have different characteristics (usually illustrated by plotting the relationship between pressure and flow on a compressor 'map') and it is difficult to produce a turbocharger which combines high efficiency with the map width needed to accommodate an engine with a wide r.p.m. and throttle range. Essential is careful matching of compressor to engine, of engine to turbine and of turbine to compressor. Whereas gas flow through the compressor diffuses, flow through the turbine does the accelerating, and turbine speed is a function of exhaust gas temperature and speed, and of pressure in the exhaust manifold. A turbine can use all the heat it can get - provided it can withstand the temperature.

Exhaust gas speed as felt by the rotor is influenced by the turbine entry nozzle: reducing the size of a nozzle will accelerate the gas at low throttle levels. On the other hand, as engine speed increases the gas can choke at the turbine entry, increasing back pressure in the manifold. That pressure rise could, in theory, eventually overtake the pressure in the inlet manifold. Further, rising back pressure tends to reduce volumetric efficiency.

In practice, a pressure relief valve is usually fitted to bleed excess pressure from the exhaust manifold once charge air pressure reaches a given level. The common diaphragm operated exhaust wastegate is thus a pressure differential sensing device, with a spring loaded poppet valve to bye-pass gas from the turbine entry once boost pressure reaches a required level.

Clearly, the speed of the turbine is the speed of the compressor. Centrifugal forces increase as the square of rotational speed but air is light stuff and in practice the compressor has to run at high speed before anything much happens in the way of significant boost. At low to medium engine speed boost will be modest, particularly as the inlet pressure build up has to carefully avoid surge. However, as revs rise pressure will start to rise disproportionately and power will climb quickly and steeply. In the worst case there will be a sudden inrush of power that the driver will find very hard to cope with. Herein lies the importance of the wastegate if a more civilised engine is desired: given the right turbocharger, the wastegate allows a desired level of manifold pressure to be achieved at medium engine speed, bleeding off the excess at higher speeds.

As we have noted, power is a function of work done on the power stroke (brake mean effective pressure (b.m.e.p.) which, in effect, is an engine's torque) and engine speed. Since the turbocharger increases b.m.e.p. for greatest benefit it will be carefully matched to an engine's torque curve, with revs rather than boost used to extract maximum power. As far as possible the turbo engine will be 'tuned' via the wastegate to maintain the desired boost level constantly on a given circuit. However, on almost any road racing circuit there will be corners for which the throttle has to be backed off to the extent that there is insufficient exhaust gas energy to keep the turbine spinning fast enough to keep the compressor within its useful working range.

Opening the throttle again will not instantly speed up the rotor assembly due mainly to the inertia of the assembly. The time spent reaching useful compressor speed is known as throttle lag - an inevitable delay between pressing the throttle pedal and power arriving at the rear wheels. Harsh power delivery and throttle lag are inherent problems of exhaust gas turbo-supercharging. It is important to keep charge plumbing and exhaust primaries short to minimise lag. The entire engine and turbo system package has to be designed as an integral component and a key element of this is the plenum chamber above the inlet tracts which balances charge air prior to induction. It is very difficult to design an inlet manifold plenum chamber that will get equal flow to each port.

The turbocharged engine's geometric compression ratio is invariably lowered since a forced charge effectively increases the ratio. Further, the entire cylinder capacity - including the combustion chamber volume - accepts the pressurised air, hence effectively engine capacity is increased, more so as the compression ratio is reduced. The turbo engine has, in effect, its compression ratio varying with boost and even if the pressurised charge is cooled cylinder temperatures will be higher than in the atmospheric engine. Heat control is a major challenge posed by the turbo engine.

The Renault turbo engine arrived in Formula One in 1977 yet as late as 1982 Keijo Rosberg was able to win the World Championship equipped with the fifteen year old normally aspirated Cosworth DFV engine. An engine that tumbled hopelessly out of contention in the mid Eighties following major strides in turbo engine development.

Turbocharged engines were confined to half the 3.0 litre capacity of the well established four valve per cylinder, d.o.h.c. British V8 that had so effectively exploited the concept - a new concept in the mid Sixties - of a flat piston crown and a shallow pent roof combustion chamber. From the outset the DFV had produced exceptional torque and gradual increase in peak power speed had helped take it from 400b.h.p. to an early Eighties figure of 510b.h.p. which represents no less than 170b.h.p. per litre (not far off the total output of an early Sixties 1.5 litre V8 engine).

To overthrow the long reign of the DFV the

new generation turbo engines had to produce more than twice its power per litre. A turbocar needed more cooler surface area creating additional drag and more fuel for internal engine cooling, adding weight. As we have noted, compressing any gas tends to increase its temperature as well as its pressure, any rise in temperature being at the expense of density. Charge air pressurisation was thus potentially at the expense of high charge temperature while since the denser charge effectively increased the compression ratio, this also added heavily to the engine's thermal loading.

In response, from early on Renault had found it necessary to feed the compressed charge air through an aftercooler to reduce charge temperature and regain potential density, this move effectively doubling the car's radiator surface area. Nevertheless, the effective increase in compression ratio led to worryingly high temperatures in the combustion chamber. There was then a real danger of exceeding the maximum thermal loading that the engine could endure - this is set by the resistance of pistons, rings, valves and valve seats to thermodynamic stress.

Pouring fuel through the engine had a beneficial cooling effect and was one response. If fuel is well atomised it will vaporise inside the cylinder. As a liquid changes into vapour it absorbs heat (called latent heat) which it obtains from its surroundings and thus vaporisation within the cylinder has a beneficial cooling effect on the combustion chamber. Nevertheless, running rich could only do so much. Renault had to do a lot of pioneering work in conjunction with specialist suppliers such as piston manufacturer Mahle and ring producer Goetze. Out of this came innovations such as the oil gallery piston. At first piston cooling was achieved by a simple spray to the underside of the crown. With increasing boost came the gallery - a circular oil channel set within the piston under the crown, a little way in from the ring belt. Oil was sprayed into the gallery through an access hole and circulated within it as the piston reciprocated through the so called 'cocktail shaker' effect, escaping again through a second hole.

The oil gallery piston was an important step in coaxing more power through increased charge

pressurisation but Renault was limited in its potential for really high boost by the heat intolerance of petrol. Back in the Thirties and Forties supercharged Grand Prix engines had made great strides through the exploitation of alcohol based fuel. Alcohol fuel was less heat intolerant - as indicated by its significantly higher octane rating - while its high latent heat of vaporisation offered an important internal cooling effect. Its disadvantage was a low calorific value. The calorific value of a fuel indicates the quantity of heat liberated when one unit is burned with oxygen. A low calorific value clearly implies that more is required - those old supercharged engines were notoriously thirsty.

Although alcohol fuel was unavailable to Renault, the very act of injecting the mandatory 102 octane petrol, cool and well atomised into the charge air offered a degree of internal cooling as it vaporised inside the cylinder, though its latent heat value was lower. Clearly then, running rich helped drop charge, combustion and exhaust temperatures, the latter effect kind on the turbine. Further, running 50% or more above the chemically correct mixture was known to reduce the tendency to detonation or pre-ignition of a petrol-fed turbo engine.

Controlled burning is only possible within certain limits defined by combustion chamber temperature, charge temperature and mean effective compression ratio. Due to the heat intolerance of petrol uncontrolled burning - the inefficient 'knocking effect' of detonation and its mechanically destructive ally pre-ignition - is the ever present danger inherent in turbocharging.

Detonation occurs when a portion of the mixture, usually near the exhaust valves, reaches a critical temperature and burns spontaneously, interfering with the progressive spread of the flame front. In the case of pre-ignition, a portion of the mixture ignites prior to ignition from the plug, due to hot spots in the chamber. Pre-ignition, which can follow from the occurrence of detonation, is the most serious form of uncontrolled burning: it causes a rapid rise in cylinder temperature and, sustained for more than a few seconds, is the easiest way to melt a piston crown.

In 1982 Ferrari introduced the concept of water

injection. The process of injecting water into the charge air had a beneficial cooling effect. Further, for reasons that had no format, text book explanation, the influence of steam was to act as an anti-detonant, allowing the mixture to be weakened back towards chemically correct and higher boost to be run, increasing power. Pre war, turbocharged aero engines had used the simple yet effective technique of water injection to get heavier payloads off the ground.

"Power boosting additives" were specifically banned from Formula One fuel but Ferrari argued that mere water could not be considered such an additive and there was no theoretical basis on which to prove otherwise. To remain competitive Renault - ever cautious in its interpretation of the regulations - could but follow Ferrari with water injection in 1983. The three main turbo engines of 1983, the Renault V6, the Ferrari V6 and the BMW in line four, were well matched for much of the season. Then, at Zandvoort, BMW surged ahead. Moving beyond petrol and water, BMW's genial Technical Director Paul Rosche had found the recipe for Elixir.

Formula One technical regulations restricted fuel to: "petrol having the following characteristics - maximum 102 octane; maximum 2% oxygen and 1% hydrogen by weight, the remaining 97% consisting exclusively of hydrocarbons and not containing any alcohols, nitrocompounds or other power boosting additives". Surprisingly, in spite of its apparent exactness, that definition of 102 octane petrol left the clever fuel chemist a tremendous amount of scope in the face of high density charge air.

The regulations did not specifically demand that Formula One cars run regular European pump petrol. Strictly speaking, "petrol" is but the European name given to refined petroleum (or a synthetic substitute produced by chemical process) and this substance can take different forms. The act of refining petroleum produces many different liquid hydrocarbons and there are over 200 chemicals present in pump petrol, which varies from manufacturer to manufacturer and from country to country. The chemist was able to ensure the presence of the precise hydrocarbons which, while not recognised "power boosting additives" work particularly well in the turbo engine.

Examples of hydrocarbons derived from petroleum are octane, toluene and aniline. Octane is commonly found in pump petrol, unlike toluene which was found to be far more useful to the turbo engine as boost rose. While low boost (as run by aero spark-ignition engines and Renault early on) tends to speed up the combustion process, the higher boost levels reached by 1983 (in excess of 2.5 bar absolute) were found to have the reverse effect. Nevertheless, working with toluene, the chemist was able to brew a legal fuel that burned more rapidly, which generated more heat energy and which had a higher resistance to detonation. In effect it was a far higher octane fuel but it came from the same base as European pump petrol and it registered only 102 octane on the mandatory slow speed, low load laboratory RON ratings test.

Rosche later told the author he had tried water injection on the dyno but had found it far more beneficial to concentrate upon fuel. BASF subsidiary Winterschall produced the pioneering toluene based fuel for him and boost was set to soar. Formula One engine builders soon dubbed it 'rocket fuel', and with good reason. In 1983 turbo engines rarely crossed the threshold of 3.0 bar, even in qualifying. Yet over the next couple of years boost went as high as 5.4 bar without detonation. In qualifying trim the rugged BMW four produced more power than Rosche's Munich dyno could measure - estimates reached beyond 1300b.h.p.

Cosworth arrived with a turbo V6 to supersede the DFV in 1985 and, for all its rich experience of racing engines, was amazed at the potential of the product of the mid Eighties Formula One chemist. "With rocket fuel 750b.h.p. was the minimum rather than the maximum power", the duly impressed Chief Racing Engine Designer Geoff Goddard told the author. Rocket fuel was not only potent, it was also heavy. The brew could be made much denser than pump petrol, packing more energy into a tank of given capacity. That was very significant given that fuel rationing was introduced in 1984.

The rationing was by volume, not weight. The maximum 220 litres of dense toluene fuel represented significantly more energy than 220 litres of pump petrol. Further, its higher detonation threshold allowed a higher compression ratio, releasing more power from a given boost level. This was further assisted by computer control of the ignition and injection systems, as pioneered pre-'84 by Ferrari and BMW. The higher compression toluene-fuelled engine was more fuel efficient than the early Grand Prix turbo engine and in spite of its fixed capacity fuel ration could race at far higher boost. In the face of rocket fuel the Cosworth DFV was dead.

Nevertheless, while fuel rationing couldn't save the old guard, it gave the runaway turbo engine a very hard time. For the first time it became imperative to run lean. A new level of thermodynamic stress was duly experienced and it took a lot of development work, and generous cooling and aftercooling provision merely to make the engine and turbocharger survive. To win it was necessary to extract the maximum amount of potential heat energy from the limited capacity fuel tank and to turn that into useful work at the crankshaft. That implied running right on the verge of detonation without actually suffering piston crown or turbine melt down.

In this respect the micro computer based engine management system was crucial. Fuelling and ignition control had come under the spotlight with the advent of turbocharging. The turbo engine needed an injection system that was responsive to boost pressure as well as throttle opening and engine speed. Renault started out with modified Kugelfischer mechanical injection, a pneumatic device sensing plenum pressure and rotating a bone-shaped "3D" cam which also moved along its main axis in response to throttle opening.

This mechanical injection system produced compromise fuelling. The mixture always had to be sufficiently rich to avoid overheating disasters and was often unnecessarily rich. A more sophisticated control system could help make the engine more responsive - a crucial consideration given the turbo engine's inherent throttle lag - and more economical.

Ferrari pioneered electro-mechanical injection in the early Eighties and by 1984 all engines were running electro-mechanical or fully electronic injection. With an electro-mechanical system an electronic control unit (ECU) takes readings from a variety of engine sensors and controls a servo motor which operates the cam on the mechanical metering unit. A fully electronic system has a similar ECU controlling solenoid-operated injector triggers, determining the precise timing and duration of each injection pulse. The fully electronic system offers more precise injection control but the solenoid injectors cannot work at such high pressure as conventional injectors and thus the atomisation of the fuel is likely to be inferior.

The ECU is based on a micro-processor and in essence consists of two chips: a RAM (Random Access Memory) chip to do the calculations and a plug-in EPROM (Erasable, Programmable, Read Only Memory) chip to dictate the injection control appropriate to any given combination of sensors. These dictates are determined following extensive dyno testing - backed by track tests - and collectively are known as a map. The map is a three dimensional picture of the engine's ideal operational conditions. A plug in EPROM facility allows for easy switching between alternative maps.

In a full engine management system the ECU controls both the injection and the ignition timing. Bosch was first with a full engine management system - Bosch Motronic - which it developed in electro-mechanical injection guise for BMW and in fully electronic guise for Porsche. The Motronic managed BMW four and Porsche V6 set the pace in 1984 with the Porsche engine winning most of the races.

The BMW engine's greatest weakness was its large single turbocharger. The Porsche V6 ran two smaller, higher revving turbochargers, one per bank. Turbocharger development had progressed rapidly since the arrival of Renault in Formula One - the work helping to significantly cut lag - but, as we have seen, 1984 presented new demands. The BMW turbocharger did not stand up well enough to those demands and subsequently BMW switched from usual supplier KKK to Garrett to get special development work done. Nevertheless, Porsche continued to rule the roost in 1985 - until the rise of Honda...

The photographs on the preceding pages show the 1988 Honda-McLaren in Prost's hands at Monte Carlo (page 2) and in Senna's hands at Rio (page 7). The model is seen uncloaked in the pits at Spa Francorchamps (page 9). The colour photographs on the following pages show, in order, Prost at Detroit, Senna at Monza, Prost at Rio, Senna at Francorchamps and Senna at Detroit.

BACKGROUND

Living Dangerously

BMW and Brabham pointed the way. As is described in the 'Origins' section, BMW introduced the computer controlled, 'rocket fuel' addicted turbo-supercharged engine. Having thus unlocked the full potential of turbocharging, partner Brabham later produced the first ever low line car of the high boost era, drastically reclining the driver to the benefit of rear wing operation. These major advances in engine technology and chassis aerodynamics played key roles in turbocar performance through the mid to late Eighties. Significantly, 1988 would see the culmination of them in the form of the virtually unbeatable Honda-McLaren turbo.

When BMW introduced 'rocket fuel' in 1983, Honda was just starting to put a toe in the water. It was, however, no stranger to Formula One. In the mid Sixties the giant Japanese motorcycle manufacturer had advertised its expansion into the car market with a series of powerful atmospheric Formula One and Two engines. Drawing heavily upon motorcycle racing practice, these units took engine speed to new heights, won the last race of the 1.5 litre Grand Prix formula at Mexico in 1965, the 1967 (3.0 litre) Italian Grand Prix and dominated (1.0 litre) Formula Two in 1966, taking 11 consecutive wins. Formula Two was the arena to which Honda returned when it resumed motor racing in 1980.

The displacement limit was now 2.0 litres and the new Honda engine was an 80 degree V6 with an iron block and gear driven d.o.h.c. four valve, single plug aluminium heads. It was the work of a team of young engineers guided by Yoshio Nakamura and Nobuhiko Kawamoto. Nakamura had designed the Sixties race engines and was now a consultant to Honda while Kawamoto had worked on those engines as a young engineer and had since risen to the post of President of Honda's extensive Wako (near Tokyo) based

Research and Development operation. A major motivation behind Honda's involvement in racing was the training of young engineers. Another key aim, aside from flag waving, was to extend the frontiers of its technical knowledge.

Kawamoto later told *Motoring News* that he chose to produce a Formula Two engine with the same bore as the 2.0 litre normally aspirated version of the BMW in line four which then dominated the European Championship, but with six cylinders, "so theoretically we could get one and a half times the power". Of course, stroke length as well as piston area determines total power output: Honda was implicitly looking for higher speed from a significantly shorter stroke.

The chosen 80 degree vee angle reflected the experience of Honda's 80 degree vee CX500 motorcycle engine and chassis installation considerations (though the engine was somewhat untidily packaged). There was no official Press Information pack and precise engine specifications were not released. The dimensions are thought to have been 90mm. x 52.3mm - a stroke: bore ratio of 0.58.

The heart of this new Honda engine was apparently conventional enough featuring a (Cosworth-style) flat piston crown and shallow valve angle pent roof combustion chamber. Intriguingly, though, tall and widely spaced cam covers told of an unconventional system of valve actuation - via finger cam followers. The 1966 Honda Formula Two engine had run finger followers, the company traditionally favouring the system whereas ever since the Fifties other bespoke race engines had almost invariably employed direct valve actuation through inverted bucket tappets.

Honda's experience did not support the view that direct operation allows a valve to follow its

cam with greater precision. Of course, direct operation of bucket tappets was more compact, keeping the centre of gravity down. Finger followers increased camshaft height but offered Honda a number of advantages. The weight and oil drag of the inverted bucket were avoided, as was its enclosure of the springs, which could run at a more equable temperature in the open. More importantly, Honda had more scope for coil spring design enabling it to provide for higher cam loads. That opened up the possibility of higher valve accelerations, smoothing the quest for higher engine speeds.

Engine power, as we have noted, is a function of torque and speed. The limit of engine speed is stress: as speed rises, eventually there comes a point at which either the piston assembly or the valve train will suffer a stress-related failure. With its finger follower system, Honda was able to provide a valve train capable of withstanding a higher level of stress. Honda's Sixties race engines had also featured the use of roller bearings for low friction. However, it had subse-

quently found plain thinwall bearings equally as effective without the weight penalty and complication. The new engine shunned rollers.

Aside from its finger followers the 1980 V6 was a conventional enough design and it was run as two three-cylinder engines sharing a common crankshaft (having three rather than six con rod journals). This arrangement was to the benefit of exhaust tuning potential on the principle of interference. It meant that each bank had even firing intervals of 240 degrees with the left hand bank firing the 80 degrees retard afforded by the cylinder configuration after the right hand bank.

Considering the engine as a whole, there was a firing interval of 80 degrees, then one of 160 degrees repeated three times instead of six equal firing intervals of 120 degrees throughout one complete 720 degree four stroke cycle. The uneven disposition of power impulses made for pronounced power plant vibration that would have been unacceptable in a road going vehicle. The Honda V6 race engine was fired by the usual (in racing) capacitor discharge (CD)-type ignition system and was fuelled by a Lucas mechanical injection system. This injection system was that employed by the six cylinder Triumph 2.5PI road car rather than the more sophisticated four/eight cylinder 'shuttle metering' racing system as used on the Cosworth DFV.

Honda's new generation Formula Two engine started its competition career with Ron Tauranac's Woking-based Ralt Cars factory team in mid 1980. Tauranac had been Brabham's designer in the days when 'Black Jack' used Honda power to crush his Formula Two opposition. Since Honda had no experience of ground effect technology it had sent Tauranac a mock up of the V6, asking for an adaptation of his regular four cylinder customer chassis. Having produced the chassis, Tauranac had been asked to race it. Kawamoto brought over the power units and a group of keen young Japanese technicians. They based themselves in the Rugby workshops of Engine Developments Ltd, a company co-owned by engine wizard John Judd and the man he had worked for in the Sixties: Jack Brabham.

Judd and Tauranac helped steer the early development of the V6. The fuel injection system needed development and from the chassis point of view the exhaust system was wrong, the

The 1966 Honda Formula Two engine featured valve actuation via finger cam followers. These were employed again in 1980 (though not as levers) unlike the torsion bar valve springs also evident here.

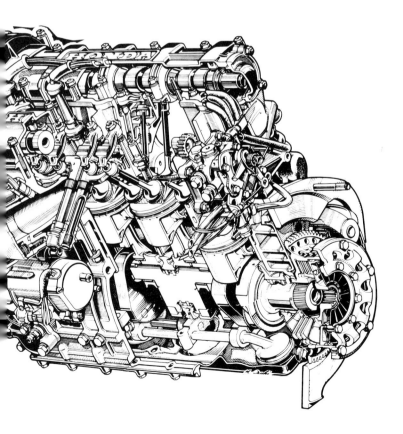

primary pipes encroaching upon space needed for the ground effect underwing's diffuser up-sweep. New heads were promptly produced with revised porting allowing higher exhaust manifolding. The chassis benefited and the porting - assisted by Judd - also improved the engine's breathing. Honda started out running to 10,500r.p.m. (just a little above the 80mm. stroke BMW's red line) and by 1981 was screaming to 11,500r.p.m., though the power band was some-what narrow.

In 1981 the two car Honda-Ralt team was very competitive but too often European Champion-ship race wins were lost through chassis, tyre, sometimes engine problems. Early on the pow-erful V6 had a pick up problem while a winter switch to Bosch mechanical injection should, on the basis of dyno testing, have provided more accurate throttle response but in practice the system proved too difficult to tune. Fuel over-heating was another engine development head-ache but through it all lead driver Geoff Lees rose to clinch the Formula Two crown.

The following year Honda supplied two For-mula Two teams, Ralt and Spirit. Spirit was a new organisation run by ex-March Formula Two Team Manager John Wickham and engineer Gordon Coppuck. In 1982 reliable sources dis-closed that on the Judd dyno the V6 and the rival BMW engine gave remarkably similar top end power but that the Honda boasted stronger mid range power.

Given that this was the case, the V6 was offer-ing less b.h.p. per 1000r.p.m. and thus arguably had the greater development potential. Clearly since '81 it had become more driveable. Alas, the '82 Ralt and Spirit challenges were weakened by inferior tyres. Honda had to wait until 1983 for its second title, this won by Ralt driver Jonathan Palmer. Over three full seasons the Japanese engine proved virtually unburstable, sustaining trips to 12,500r.p.m. as a matter of course and rarely failing to last a race.

Since early 1982 Honda had been working on a turbocharged derivative. Right from the outset the marque's long term aim had been a return to Grand Prix racing and with turbocharging gradu-ally ousting normally aspirated Formula One engines a short stroke version of the V6 was an obvious starting point. Before the '82 season was

out Spirit had started testing a conventionally-blown conversion in an adapted Formula Two chassis.

Tauranac had little interest in Formula One at this stage (Indy Car racing was his major unful-filled ambition, he told the author in 1981) but Wickham and Coppuck had high ambitions for their fledgling operation. They had accepted a busy Formula One test programme for 1983, the wraps officially coming off the so called RA-163-E at the March '83 Geneva Motor Show. The 163 label indicated (Formula) One six cylinder '83.

Although the RA-163-E beat the Porsche/TAG engine's unveiling at the same show by half an hour or so, it did not attempt to match the German engine's impressive launch. The author found a low key event on the Honda stand: an engine looking much like the familiar Formula Two V6 with a turbocharger system added, a few smiling Japanese faces, and a press folder containing but three stapled sheets of A4 paper and four black and white photographs. The tech-nical information, although typed double-spaced could not fill a single sheet. It admitted only: liquid cooled, four valve d.o.h.c. 80 degree V6; CD ignition; dry sump; dry multi-plate clutch; Honda Electric Fuel Injection/PGMF1 (Pro-grammed fuel injection system - developed for F2 and F1 engines and also used in City-turbo); twin KKK type K26 turbochargers; maximum output over 600b.h.p.

Much of this was fairly obvious and "over 600 b.h.p." was the going rate for the time. The external similarity to the Formula Two engine prompted the idea that Honda had retained the bore of its 2.0 litre engine - 90.0mm. implying a stroke of 39.35mm. - but this would not be confirmed for over six years. Clearly the inter-nals had been modified in response to the higher level of thermodynamic stress - oil cooling for the piston, sodium cooling for the exhaust valves, heat resistant valve seats and so forth - while the base engine could be seen to be familiar.

The then-secret finger cam followers had, of course, been carried over as witness the distinc-tive cam covers, this technology making the RA-163-E unique in Formula One. Of the few details announced at Geneva, the most interesting was Honda's early deployment of micro-computer controlled fuelling. The Porsche/TAG arrived downstairs in a Geneva Show function room equipped with Bosch mechanical injection, by way of contrast.

Already Spirit had managed to convince Honda of the wisdom of running its purpose built '83 test car - a further modified Formula Two machine - in selected races. It went on to contest six events with a single car, finishing in three, albeit well down the field. Driver Stefan Johansson reported plenty of power but within a narrow band and disconcertingly sudden in its arrival. Meanwhile Honda had been seeking a liaison with a major team for 1984. In the summer it concluded an agreement with Williams Grand Prix Engineering (WGPE) which was just about to see the last glimmer of hope of ever repeating Rosberg's '82 World Championship success with the Cosworth DFV engine disappear in a haze of computer-metered 'rocket fuel'.

Frank Williams' company had duly found its salvation in a deal with a major manufacturer committed to winning, and with a budget to match. Honda offered its costly turbo engine free of charge. However, it did not supply the cooling system, the RA-163-E units arriving virtually bare. WGPE Technical Director Patrick Head later told Racecar Engineering contributor Allan Staniforth: "We had to improvise a lot. Honda hadn't the least idea of heat generated or air consumed once the engine was in a car. We had to do the whole installation ourselves".

Nevertheless, WGPE felt it should make every effort to start racing before 1983 was out. With some furious design and build work it got its exploratory FW09 turbo car ready for the season closing South African Grand Prix. The engine was heavy but produced an impressive 650b.h.p. at 11,000r.p.m. on 3.0 bar qualifying pressure. It still went off like a bomb when the power chimed in and Rosberg confirmed that the performance was confined to a narrow band, and complained that throttle lag was pronounced. In spite of that he got his head down, took the little tested, powerful but heavy and somewhat uncivilised new car by the scruff of the neck and led it into the points, taking an impressive fifth place.

Over the winter Honda switched from KKK to bespoke IHI - Ishikawajima Harima Heavy Industries - turbochargers. European engine builders continued to rely upon the general supplier but Honda had already appreciated the importance of getting special development work done in this key area. Another key area was fuel technology: Honda had clearly understood the importance of BMW's recent breakthrough for in '84 it became one of the first to follow the Munich marque in the use of toluene. That was particularly significant in view of the 220 litre fuel ration, and so was the PGMF1 computerised fuelling, which was further developed in conjunction with Hitachi.

On toluene fuel Honda admits it ran to 3.5 bar in qualifying in 1984, power then officially 750b.h.p. at 11,000r.p.m. The power band had apparently been widened a little but the block arguably started showing signs of unhappiness at having its original output trebled. The FW09 - one of the last metal honeycomb chassis in Formula One - gained a probably undeserved reputation for understeer through lack of torsional rigidity. Undeserved since the block was fully stressed and might well have been the weak link. Indeed, block flexing might have been the root of a spectacular series of piston failures. In '84 the Honda V6 lacked good driveability and reliability.

Nevertheless, there were flashes of hope. Not least at Dallas where the track broke up, cars crashed by the dozen but Rosberg's Honda held together and his lightening reflexes kept him off the wall and in front. It was a freak victory and Honda knew it had a long way to go to produce a fully competitive engine. Flushed by its premature success it redoubled its efforts and developed a full engine management system - integrating injection and ignition control - for 1985. Further, it developed a structurally revised engine to replace the Formula Two base.

Yoshitoshi Sakurai now took overall charge as Formula One Project Leader and Chief Engineer, reporting to Kawamoto. His brief apparently was to field a new engine good enough to do the job, regardless of the cost. Reputedly Honda built 25 different engine specifications over the winter of '84/'85 as it paved the way for the bespoke (rather than converted Formula Two) unit. Higher power through increasing boost pressure was the aim, together with improvement in reliability under high boost operating conditions, particularly the reliability of the pistons and the turbines.

Williams produced a state-of-the-art chassis for '85 and had Rosberg and Nigel Mansell as drivers. Mansell had debuted the Formula Two V6 back in 1980. The new generation engine now readied for him was similar externally, having an iron block retaining the (now Porsche/TAG shared) 80 degree vee and aluminium heads sporting the characteristic high and widely spaced cam covers that told of the continuing deployment of finger followers. However, the new block skilfully employed cast-in ducts and piping to add to its structural strength and it was significantly more rigid. While the iron base provided much needed stiffness, Nikasil coated aluminium wet liners helped save weight and offered good heat rejection.

The key specification change was a significantly smaller bore - 82mm. apparently, though the exact dimension has never been confirmed. The smaller bore was necessary in the face of increasing boost and the relatively high compression ratio needed to succeed under the 220 litre fuel ration. The size of the piston crown had become a crucial consideration given the high level of thermodynamic stress. A smaller bore meant a shorter travel for the flame front and reduced the length of the primary heat path, which is from the centre of the piston crown out to the ring belt, thence via the rings to the cylinder wall and the coolant. The majority of heat must escape via this route.

Kawamoto later told journalist Christopher Hilton: "By 1985 we were beginning to understand the importance of combustion control in a turbo engine. We carried out tests with a number of different types of combustion chambers. Once combustion was well under control we could increase the boost pressure without increasing the fuel consumption and this significantly improved the engine's performance. Our own electronic engine control system was very useful... finally the development of it became more important than developing the engine itself".

The all new RA-165-E arrived mid season, at Spa Francorchamps and since that race was called off in the face of a broken track surface it made its race debut at Montreal. It won second time out, at Detroit, Rosberg taking a convincing

victory. He then took pole at Silverstone. The officially quoted 1985 power output for qualifying was 950b.h.p. at 11,500r.p.m. on a plenum pressure of 4.0 bar absolute. As usual, that was for a race engine run in qualifying trim, Honda's policy not to produce specific qualifying engines.

Perceptive ears could hear improvement in the power band and the Honda-Williams clearly was now a real force to be reckoned with. That strength coincided with the opening of a purpose-built engine 'shop within WGPE's Didcot factory. By this stage Honda had produced an ultra-sophisticated fuel read out to help the driver monitor the consumption of his 220 litres of toluene-based fuel. Towards the end of the season the overall engine height was lowered to help Williams improve the airflow to the rear wing.

And finally it all came good: three more convincing wins, at Brands Hatch, Kyalami and Adelaide confirmed the rise of Honda. In that final phase of the '85 season the Honda-Williams was the car to beat: Honda had risen to the very top. And it stayed there in 1986, eight wins to the credit of Mansell and new teammate Nelson Piquet convincingly collecting the Constructor's Cup for Williams and Honda.

The 25 litre race ration cut for '86 had been partly offset by continuing development of the toluene-based fuel that Mobil was supplying while the bore had shrunk further, to 79.0 x 50.84mm. The compression ratio was 7.4:1 and a compact combustion chamber was based around a valve angle of 39 degrees and incorporation of a squish band. A squish band causes violent displacement of the mixture as the piston reaches top dead centre, this action causing additional turbulence. Turbulence is vital to efficient combustion.

The RA-166-E ran to 11,800r.p.m. in qualifying, officially producing 1100b.h.p. from 5.0 bar and generally it offered higher race power than any other engine. These days, to win it was necessary to run on the very verge of detonation and Honda appeared to be able to live more dangerously than anyone. Moreover, reliability was extremely good. Asked to explain Honda's winning edge, Renault Technical Director Bernard Dudot told the author: "they had good ex-

The 1985 Honda RA-165-E was, from mid season, a new generation engine with a significantly smaller bore. It got the Honda-Williams up to speed, then the combination was extremely difficult to beat...

perience of control of detonation - all aspects, combustion chamber design, air intake, fuel, electronic control and so forth. Perhaps Honda was a little closer on each point".

Interesting turbocharger experiments included Variable Geometry Scrolls - VGS - and adjustable inlet nozzles for the turbines. VGS employs a ring of adjustable vanes around the turbine wheel to increase gas velocity as engine speed falls off. The adjustable inlet nozzle has a similar effect. However, the extra weight and complexity of these developments was not found worthwhile. These days, while the compressor wheel was still aluminium, the turbine wheel was Inconel. Inconel is an ultra-high temperature tolerant alloy that is very hard to work.

Honda also employed an unusual aftercooler bye-pass to send charge air direct from the compressor to the plenum under certain conditions. The direct route promoted improved throttle response and fuel economy (the warmer air assisting atomisation) at the expense of power and an increased thermal loading. The bye-pass control was incorporated into the engine management system, together with boost control. The new boost control facility constantly man-

aged the opening of the wastegate valve within parameters set by the driver.

There was a deceptively simple and "driver friendly" four position race boost control. Linked very sensitively to the management system this electronically altered the complete map according to the driver's wishes. The switch gave a choice of "fuel saver", low race boost, high race boost and overtaking power. The accurate fuel read out, a telemetry system sending engine management signals direct to the pits for constant monitoring by the Honda engineers and a pits to car radio helped the driver make the most of this strong tactical weapon.

For 1987 Honda moved out of the WGPE factory to a new base at Langley on the edge of Slough from which it prepared engines for both Williams and Team Lotus. Williams continued with Mansell and Piquet while Lotus ran Ayrton Senna and Japanese Formula Two multi-Champion Satoru Nakajima in a Gerard Ducarouge designed car that featured Group Lotus' computer controlled 'Active' suspension system. The four cars continued Honda's domination of Formula One, Williams generally out in front.

Lotus didn't get the benefit of Williams' insight into the cooling requirements of the Honda engine and lost out in terms of aerodynamic efficiency until smaller aftercoolers arrived in mid season. Throughout, the revolutionary suspension system was arguably too clever for its own good: perhaps significantly, Senna only won on the Monaco and Detroit street circuits which - untypically - demanded proper suspension movement. Meanwhile, Mansell and Piquet increased WGPE's record season tally to nine wins and thus again the combination of Honda and Williams easily lifted the Constructors Cup. Piquet won the World Championship.

Thus, the new condition of 4.0 bar maximum plenum pressure - controlled by a mandatory FISA supplied pop off valve - could not prevent Honda continuing its crushing success. It had produced a total of 60 4.0 bar engines for the two teams, in four different specifications to suit varying operational conditions. A later official statement commented, "with pressure limited to 4.0 bar two aspects of engine development became very important. One aspect was to increase the engine speed to a higher limit, which was required to attain more power. The other was to develop an accurate boost control system, to keep boost at its highest possible pressure under the pop-off valve limit".

The RA-167-E ran to 12,000r.p.m. and featured a further refined engine management system. Distributorless ignition was new for '87, each plug having its own coil built into the cap. This allowed independent control of each cylinder's ignition timing for yet more refined control. Equally significant, the improved engine management system also featured the first on track use of a Lambda probe.

The Greek letter Lambda is used in Germany (where the probe was developed) as the standard symbol for air ratio - the ratio of the actual quantity of air supplied to that required for complete combustion. The function of the Lambda sensor is to detect departures from complete combustion by assessing the oxygen content of the exhaust emission. The ratio of air to fuel required for complete combustion of a given fuel is known as its stoichiometric ratio and is indicated as Lambda = 1.0. In the case of petrol the stoichiometric ratio is just about 14:1 while maximum power tends to be produced at a ratio of 1.2, or 20% rich. The very high toluene-level fuel as used by Honda from mid season had a stoichiometric ratio of 13.7:1 and maximum power was produced at a ratio of 1.23.

Honda effectively used a Lambda probe as part of a closed loop engine control system. If the injectors were not supplying the amount of fuel required to form the desired air:fuel ratio, the Lambda sensor would signal this back to the control unit, which would instantly make the appropriate correction.

The Lambda probe monitoring the RA-167-E had been pioneered for road car applications in Germany by Bosch, its introduction prompted by Seventies exhaust emission control laws. Bosch had been the first to devise a probe that was sensitive enough to allow it to be used as an engine management sensor. Road use was one thing, racing was another and it was a technical masterpiece to get a Lambda sensor to work on the exhaust manifold of a turbocharged engine producing tremendous levels of heat and pressure.

The RA-167-E's compression ratio was upped

from 7.4:1 to 8.2:1 during the course of the season and with that, in mid season Honda reached an 84% level of toluene in its 195 litre tank. The higher toluene level fuel was harder to atomise, making the charge temperature control aftercooler bye-pass particularly significant. Running to 12,000r.p.m, the 4.0 bar engine produced a solid 1010b.h.p. for qualifying given a (fully cooled) charge temperature of 40 degrees centigrade and a stoichiometric figure of 1.23. Torque was a healthy 67.7kg./m. Again Honda found superb race economy, allied to which was a continuing high level of reliability. Only at the end of the '87 season did rivals Ferrari and Cosworth catch up with Honda's 4.0 bar engine power.

Cosworth crept over 1000b.h.p. in Japan. The old DFV had been developed to produce in the region of 175b.h.p. per litre and impressively the marque's turbo engine had now matched Honda's 175b.h.p. per litre per bar boost at four times atmospheric pressure. A figure of 175b.h.p. per litre per bar boost was one thing at 2.0 bar, was quite another at 4.0 bar and mid Eighties turbo engines had run over 1000b.h.p. only pumping higher pressures.

For Cosworth, the dethroned King of race engine technology, matching Honda's power took toluene fuel similar to that run by Honda (and again from Mobil), an engine management system as powerful as that of Honda (though Cosworth was without distributorless ignition and a Lambda probe) and a very high compression ratio (though this it declined to quote). Like Honda, Cosworth had developed an advanced turbo system that made lag virtually undetectable on the ECU log. Cosworth similarly had ECU wastegate control and it boasted a unique compressor performance enhancer. The effect of this device was to gave the incoming air a pre swirl in the direction of rotation. Honda had no such system.

Unlike the Honda engine, Cosworth's compact 120 degree V6 employed an alloy block which gave adequate strength with less weight and better heat rejection than iron. The wide vee angle kept the weight low, the profile low (for good airflow to the rear wing) and made for smooth running. Cosworth had not only a similar bore to Honda (though again it would not

The first Honda-McLaren, a modified '87 MP4/3, was sent to Japan in February '88 after preliminary tests in England (commencing in December '87). Here Senna drives it at Suzuka, moving over from Lotus.

quote a precise figure) but also a similar 40 degree valve angle since keeping the valves well apart allowed more scope for valve cooling. Typically, the Cosworth valves were driven through bucket tappets.

Otherwise, in mechanical terms there was little significant difference between British and Japanese 4.0 bar engine technology. Thus, for Cosworth as for Honda, forged aluminium alloy oil cooled pistons reciprocated in Nikasil coated aluminium liners, driving a nitrided steel crankshaft though a steel gudgeon pin and a titanium con rod. Valves were steel and sodium cooled and valve seats were bronze based. Ferrari employed similar technology, too, in its iron block 90 degree V6, and like Honda it had a distributorless ignition system. The differences between the rival engines were hard to evaluate in performance terms and arguably the most important performance factor was the effectiveness of the engine management system.

Cosworth worked with sponsor Ford USA's Motorola division while Ferrari worked with Marelli Weber, a fellow member of the Fiat Group. Meanwhile, the Bosch Motronic managed Porsche/TAG engine appeared to have

dropped somewhat in the power stakes after three World Championship titles - Lauda in '84, Prost in '85 and '86. Nevertheless, the Porsche/TAG-McLaren had come close to giving Prost a third title in 1987 as Mansell and Piquet shared out the WGPE points.

McLaren International (MI) had been the most consistently successful team since the advent of fuel rationing in Formula One. At first this was attributed to the Porsche/TAG engine's lead in engine management technology with the Bosch fully electronic system yet as the more heavily funded Honda engine moved ahead on race performance MI refused to be beaten, as witness Prost's '86 title. The secret of its success was in a superb package, in which all the elements were strong - chassis, engine, drivers, engineering and team management.

Tragically, early in '87 Frank Williams was paralysed by a road accident. Although during the course of the season he was able to return to certain duties it was clear that the management of WGPE had, for the time being, been weakened. Honda could not have been happy with the way things had developed at Didcot in 1987, the team facing a serious breakdown in the relationship between its two star drivers and apparently an unhealthy amount of internal strife.

Meanwhile, there had arisen a new opportunity for Honda. Through the Eighties MI had grown to become one of the best equipped and best staffed of all Formula One racing teams and it had in its sights to become a broad ranging advanced engineering facility. It offered Honda the attractive prospect of sharing in this next phase of its impressive development. It also offered arguably the two fastest drivers in the world for 1988: Prost and Senna.

After its difficult 1987 season, Lotus indicated it would be happy to run Honda's World Champion and (again) its token Japanese driver - in spite of Nakajima's lack of speed in '87. In contrast, it appears that, given the same option WGPE indicated that it would rather go its own way. On the face of it, Frank Williams liked the look of a generous golden handshake (plus continuing behind the scenes help) more than Honda's offer for 1988. As with the parting from Spirit, Honda acted properly and in a gentlemanly fashion, although certain sections of the press did not wish to see it that way.

Honda's new partner had recently changed its Technical Director. MI had been founded upon the design and development skill of John Barnard plus the management expertise of Ron Dennis. Having spent seven years working for the company, Barnard had felt the need for a new challenge and towards end of '86 he had moved to Ferrari. For MI Barnard had pioneered the carbon fibre monocoque back in 1980 then, following the flat bottom ruling of 1983, an approach to aerodynamics that had been imitated by most other vee-engined cars. Meanwhile, Gordon Murray - who came in to replace Barnard - had gone a different route with his in line four engined Brabham designs. For Honda, McLaren would produce a car influenced by both avenues of development.

The flat bottom ruling required the entire width of the underbody between front and rear wheels to be a uniformly flat surface. This did not, however, wipe out the concept of ground effect aerodynamics, it merely restricted the scope for underwing design. The immediate effect of the flat bottom ruling was a return to pronounced, multi-element front and rear wings. However, it was still possible to win some downforce through underbody air acceleration.

Given a vee six engine, Barnard showed how it should be done. His solution required a large planform area, with full width sidepods and the mandatory flat undertray extending as closely as possible to the rear wheels. Behind the rear wheel axis Barnard set a diffuser section, rising either side of the gearbox and extending to the limit of rear overhang. In effect, the flat bottom area became a venturi throat. Each of the diffuser inlets provided a focus for the general influx of air characteristic of an unsealed, low ground clearance underbody region.

Air accelerated as it squeezed under the pod floor, got another 'kick' as it squeezed between the rear wheels; yet another as it funnelled into the diffuser. Acceleration of air into the upsweeps caused the biggest pressure drop. The local effect of the rear wing (set as far back as possible) helped pull air through the underbody region, and the action of the diffusers was further assisted by exhaust discharge. However, Barnard's underwing only worked really well as part of a total aerodynamic package which featured a conspicuous 'coke bottle' rear body shape. The sidepods blended into a tightly waisted engine and transaxle cover leaving plenty of space between the rear shrouding and the rear wheels.

Barnard's rear body shape interacted well with the full length underwing, it left the upper surface of the diffusers exposed and thus 'active' and it ensured a clean airflow to the rear wing. There was a complex interaction between the underwing, the rear wing and the characteristic tail shrouding and both internal and external overbody airflows were important to the working of the overall package. Everything right down to front and rear wing side plates had to be very carefully designed as part of a complex aerodynamic system.

Even with an effective underwing as prescribed by Barnard front and rear wings had to produce over 50% of total downforce. This was evident by the continuing deployment of two and three element wings. Happily, pronounced front wings could be made to interact well with the operation of a flat bottom car's underwing, in effect by sweeping oncoming air away from the underbody region so as to assist the quest to reduce pressure. Air was channelled towards the sidepod inlets. A high volume of air was required for cooling purposes and thus the sidepod ducts wanted all the air they could get. These flows caused drag and there was an important trade off between drag reduction and sufficient cooling.

While an adequate sidepod feed was important, so was proper discharge of hot air from the radiators - both in terms of cooling efficiency and the operation of the overall aerodynamic package. For example, the aftercoolers discharged through the narrow tail but Barnard threw air from the water radiators (one each side) out through the top of the respective pod - alongside the central fuel tank - these flows enhancing the feed to the rear wing.

Behind the cockpit coaming, the fuel tank and engine were shrouded by a bubble-shaped dorsum which left only the tip of the roll hoop exposed and did not cling to the top of the engine but again was carefully shaped to play its part in the operation of the overall aerodynamic package. It was all very complex. Further, in general terms the car was run as low as possible, not only to enhance the operation of the front wings (which worked in ground effect) and the underwing but also to minimise drag-inducing underbody turbulence and to keep the centre of gravity as low as possible.

For optimum effect the car was run raked, nose down, to set the flat portion of the underwing at the optimum 'angle of attack' while presenting the air with the right size of mouth. Clearly front and rear ground clearances were crucial. The Barnard solution was consequently extremely pitch sensitive and this called for stiff springing, particularly at the front end to keep the rise and fall of the less heavily weighted nose under control.

Through the mid Eighties Barnard's widely copied McLaren MP4 package gradually evolved under his direction, although outwardly it remained essentially unchanged. Its efficiency nevertheless improved, primarily following the lessons of extensive hours of wind tunnel modelling. Aside from response to changes in the technical regulations it was a case of subtle refinement of the same basic package offering progressively increasing downforce.

For 1985 rear wing size had to be reduced and in response Barnard shortened the sidepods by 100mm. and narrowed the tail by 33mm. Those bodywork modifications were hard to spot but during the season greatly enlarged front brake ducts were a very obvious change. They were as tall as the wheel rim and clung closely to it. They had a significant effect on the overall airflow and were subsequently outlawed.

With the reduced size 195 litre fuel tank the driver was reclined a little but again there was no outward change. The only significant alteration to the original prescription came in 1987, following Barnard's departure. His former assistant Steve Nichols switched from top to side venting for the water radiators, lowering the height of the pods. Introduced by Lotus in 1985, side venting was not an automatic gain: one body of opinion had it that top vents created more downforce by throwing air towards the rear wing while another had it that side vents created more downforce by clearing the flow to the wing. Nichols also deflated the characteristic

swollen dorsum, his overall approach following late Eighties trends towards increased mass airflow to the rear wing.

Gordon Murray had set the ball rolling in 1986. He had never followed the Barnard Book of Flat Bottom Aerodynamics. For a start, given the BMW in line four engine Murray had only one exhaust pipe to play with and thus he could not have 'blown' both of the twin diffuser tunnels. Murray found that full length diffusers would not work effectively without exhaust activation and he also had the disadvantage of a bulky engine which did not allow him to create a proper Barnard-style 'coke bottle' tail plan.

Instead, Murray opted for short 'flip ups' flanking the gearbox at the back of the mandatory flat bottom area. Again, the upsweep acted as a focus for the accelerating underbody airflow and worked in conjunction with the rear wing. However, it was designed to work in conjunction with a relatively high and wide rear shroud.

An open back, open floor, otherwise enclosed space at the rear of a low ground clearance car will tend to feel low pressure within as the car passes through the air. However, unless positive steps are taken to avoid it, the creation of downforce will be spoiled to a large degree by the migration of high pressure air in through the open back. In the case of the Brabham the flip ups, in effect, fed into an open back, open floor space (this space formed by the bodywork encasing the transaxle) which worked in conjunction with the rear wing. The extractor effect of the wing stopped the migration of high pressure air into this under-tail region and the combined effect of the wing and the carefully designed rear shroud pulled air through the flip ups.

Murray's Brabham solution was nevertheless compromised by the bulk of the BMW engine. Murray says of 1985: "we tried for the whole year and couldn't find more downforce. We needed a 10% bigger wing but the greater depth of such a wing would have 'hidden' it behind the rear deck". In the final analysis it was a fundamental problem of the shape of the engine package and the only possible solution was to modify that shape. During the course of 1985 BMW accepted the concept of a 'lay down' version of its four cylinder engine with the block canted over at 72 degrees from the vertical, in true Indy Roadster style.

Given that commitment Murray started exploring chassis possibilities. He concluded that he should get everything as low as possible to match the vastly reduced height of the lay down BMW package. That meant reclining the driver to a degree unheard of since the low power, low 'g' force 1.5 litre cars of the early Sixties. Jim Clark lay right back in the trendsetting Lotus 25/33 monocoque chassis but since the advent of larger 3.0 litre engines in 1966 seating positions had invariably been more upright. Indeed, given high power and high downforce it was widely assumed that the driver needed to sit up to get sufficient purchase on the steering wheel.

Piquet tried a mock up of the Brabham BT55's radical driving position and felt that it ought to be acceptable. He then moved over to WGPE leaving Murray to cross his fingers: only track testing could confirm that it would work. The great advantage of a low line fuselage was enhanced flow to the rear wing. There was also a useful 10% reduction in frontal area. In spite of a significantly lower fuselage the reduction was not greater than 10% since the car naturally retained a big rear wing. Looking at the car head on, the reduction in cross-sectional area was to be found in a gap between the underside of the wing and the low lying rear deck, either side of the smaller shadow projected by a slimmer headrest/roll bar. Far more important than the frontal area gain was the fact that the low line fuselage left the rear wing in cleaner air.

Since the low line BMW-Brabham still provided only one exhaust pipe to play with, and since the lay-down engine was too wide for a 'coke bottle' tail, the BT55 retained Murray's usual pattern of underwing. Nevertheless, early wind tunnel tests revealed a major 30% leap in downforce, with an improved lift:drag ratio thanks to greater wing efficiency and to the reduction in frontal area. There was also a beneficial reduction in the height of the centre of gravity. And thankfully, the initial track tests confirmed that the drivers could indeed cope with the fully reclined seating position.

Alas, the BT55 was not a success on the track. The engine ran hot in its new guise and the quest for better cooling badly compromised the aerodynamic package. A special transverse transmission to service the offset crankshaft proved troublesome, costing valuable pre-season test running. The cooling modifications took weight off the rear and together with an extremely long wheelbase reduced front to rear weight transfer to the detriment of traction. Worse, the engine mysteriously refused to pick up cleanly, possibly due to a scavenging problem.

Properly sorted the BT55 cornered quickly in spite of its compromised aerodynamics but, though it had a high top speed, throughout the season it suffered a fundamental lack of acceleration. BMW and Brabham never did get to the root of the engine temperature problem, nor of the lack of acceleration. The BT55's difficulties split the Brabham team and late in the season Murray moved to MI to replace Barnard.

Murray took with him an appreciation of the worth of the low line concept It was a worth that the BT55's troubles had perhaps concealed to the outside world. Although some designers made half hearted attempts to recline the driver there was not a true low line car to be seen in the '87 field. Of course, a true low liner called for a very low engine and aside from the lay down BMW there was only one such, the Cosworth V6 turbo. Murray's arrival at MI was too late to significantly influence the '87 MP4/3 but was followed by the switch to Honda engines.

Aside from reducing the height of its 80 degree V6, Honda faced the task of adapting it to run under a 2.5 bar pop-off valve and to race to a 150 litre fuel ration. FISA had promised to swing the balance of power in favour of the new generation 3.5 litre 'atmo' cars for 1988, allowing the atmos a 40kg. weight advantage and unrestricted fuel. In the early Eighties turbo engines had run at around 2.5 bar on unlimited fuel yet had been hard pressed to defeat 3.0 litre 'atmo' cars. But that had been before the days of engine management systems and rocket fuel...

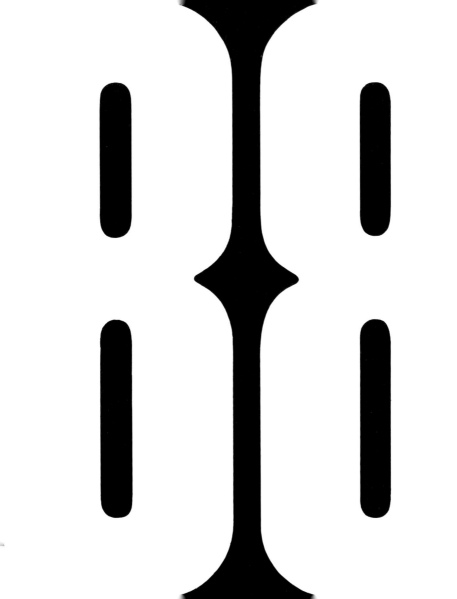

1988

Formula One Regulations

During the course of the 3.0 litre atmo era Formula One technical regulations became ever more complex and involved. Consequently, what follows can only be a brief summary of key points.

Late Eighties Formula One cars were built specifically to contest the FIA Formula 1 World Championship, a series of 16 races of 300-320km. distance with a two hour maximum duration limit. Drivers' and constructors' titles were contested, the scoring 9-6-4-3-2-1 with the best 11 scores only to count. Competitors were allowed no more than one change of make of engine during the course of a season, with each combination of chassis and engine makes scoring separately for the Constructor's Cup. The World Championship was administered by FISA on behalf of the FIA.

Only spark ignition engines of the conventional four stroke reciprocating piston type were eligible. Maximum displacement was set at 3.5 litres unsupercharged, 1.5 litres supercharged with supercharged engines having a mandatory FISA-supplied pop-off valve fitted to the plenum chamber and set to open at pressure in excess of 2.5 bar for 1988. Engines having twin plenum chambers had to be equipped with a valve on each plenum. All engines were limited to a maximum of 12 cylinders.

Eligible fuel was defined as "petrol having the following characteristics - maximum 102 (RON) octane... maximum 2% oxygen and 1% hydrogen by weight, the remaining 97% consisting exclusively of hydrocarbons and not containing any alcohols, nitrocompounds or other power boosting additives".

In-race refuelling was banned and supercharged cars only were limited to a maximum fuel tank capacity of 150 litres for 1988. Fuel chilling to reduce density, thereby squeezing a greater weight into the set tank volume was forbidden. Aftercooler water sprays (to assist charge cooling) were also illegal.

Supercharged cars had a minimum weight limit of 540kg. whereas unsupercharged cars had a limit of 500kg. All cars were limited to a maximum of four wheels, only two driven and all properly sprung. All wheels had to be external to the coachwork and the cockpit had to be open. The maximum overall wheel size was a diameter of 26" and a width of 18".

There was no limit on wheelbase or the overall length of a car but long wheelbases were generally thought undesirable. A new regulation for 1988 which stipulated that the pedals should be situated completely behind the front axle line imposed a fresh wheelbase consideration. A team could, however, avoid this by registering to run a 1987 supercharged car with its chassis "materially unchanged".

There were limits on front and rear overhang and together with specific width and height limits these restricted wing sizes and positioning while the scope for underwing design was severely restricted by the regulation calling for the bottom of the car to be flat within the wheelbase, over the distance between the front and rear tyres. Any form of skirt bridging the gap between the bottom of the chassis and the track surface was illegal. Further, wings and other aerodynamic appendages had to be rigidly secured to the sprung part of the car and had to remain immobile.

The maximum rear overhang was 600mm. and, while the maximum overall width of the car was 2150mm, the coachwork was limited to 1400mm. within the wheelbase and 1000mm. behind the rear wheel axis and above rear wheel height. These dictates plus a maximum overall height excluding the safety roll-over bar of 1000mm. limited rear wing size and position. Front wings were restricted by a maximum front overhang of 1200mm. and a maximum width of 1500mm. ahead of the front wheel axis, falling to 1100mm. above rim height. Even brake duct sizes were carefully restricted, this ruling following the appearance of 'aerodynamic' brake ducts in the mid Eighties.

The chassis had to recognise minimum cockpit dimensions and a requirement for two safety roll-over bars, one behind the driver, the other ahead of the steering wheel and reaching to steering wheel height. There was to be a 'crushable structure' to protect the fuel tank and in addition the chassis structure had to incorporate a so called "survival cell".

In essence, the survival cell legislation demanded an integral chassis box member running each side of the cockpit to a point 500mm. ahead of the driver's feet, and outside that structure protective side panels which could form each side pod's outer wall. The foremost 400mm. of each box member was not necessarily to be part of the main chassis structure - the monocoque - but was to be "solidly fixed to it". The box members had to conform to certain materials and dimensional criteria, as did the side panels. The latter were required to be at least 200mm. high and to cover at least 60% of the wheelbase length.

New for 1988 were static impact tests for the sides of the cockpit and the fuel tank region in addition to a previously required test for the nosebox.

Access to the cockpit was to be unhindered and in theory the driver had to be able to vacate the car within five seconds, without the need to remove the steering wheel. Safety belt, life support system, extinguishers for driver compartment and engine compartment, electrical circuit breakers and dual braking systems were all mandatory, each area covered by detailed requirements. Additional safety minded regulations laid down minimum requirements for fuel and oil systems and specified acceptable fluid and electrical lines. The fuel container had to be an FIA approved Kevlar-reinforced supple rubber bag located within 400mm. of the longitudinal axis of the car.

Each competitor was limited to 40 slick tyres per event with a maximum of eight for each timed practice session. In any case, lack of competition for Goodyear effectively ruled out the phenomenon of qualifying tyres in 1988 as well as removing the tyre factor from the race day equation.

The McLaren MP4/4 was the first car to follow the low line pattern of the Brabham BT55 (previous spread). The inset MP4/4 and BT55 are both pictured at post 37 Mexico City, two long years separating them

The colour photographs on the following pages show Honda McLaren turbo versus Ferrari turbo in '88. The scenes - in order - are from Paul Ricard, Monza Imola, Monaco and Monza. At Ricard Senna is seen ahead of Berger while at Monaco Berger leads Prost at Imola Senna looks for a way past him. At Monza Prost and Senna are seen ahead of Berger and Alboreto, then Senna alone is seen leading the red cars

Computer Business

On the face of it 2.5 bar and 150 litres was a heavy double-handicap for the turbo runners but recent developments in fuel and engine management technology made the impact of the new regulations difficult for those without the right research facilities to accurately predict. Honda did its sums and concluded that either a new generation atmo engine or a modified 1.5 litre turbo engine could out-perform a conventional atmo engine, as typified by the enlarged capacity Cosworth DFV used by Tyrrell to win the 3.5 litre category in 1987.

For 1988 it was clear that all atmo runners would employ either the classic Cosworth engine or an alternative V8 developed by John Judd's Engine Developments concern with support from Honda. The Judd V8 had started life as a joint project with Honda to produce a lightly turbocharged 2.65 litre Indy Car engine. Honda supported Judd's subsequent 3.5 litre unblown derivative to help keep Formula One grids full: the Japanese giant took from the sport and gave in return. Like the Sixties-designed Cosworth V8, the tightly budgeted Judd V8 'customer engine' ran to 11,000r.p.m. and produced around 600b.h.p. - a shade under 175b.h.p. per litre.

Honda knew that a new generation engine heavily funded by a major manufacturer for a works supported team could be coaxed to run to a significantly higher speed, producing 650b.h.p. or more. However, not until 1989 when only 3.5 litre engines would be admitted would Cosworth, Ferrari, Renault and other major factories be ready to pitch in with such equipment. Honda chose to bring in its own new generation 3.5 litre offering at the same time. The alternative of developing a super-frugal, low boost turbo for 1988 promised important technical lessons. Honda

did not consider turbocharging to be a long term blind alley and this was the sort of challenge its Research and Development operation relished.

The 1988 Honda turbo was developed by a team of engineers led by Osamu Goto, moving up to replace Yoshitoshi Sakurai as Formula One Project Leader and Chief Engineer. A racing enthusiast, Goto had worked on the Grand Prix programme since 1984, having formerly been employed on emission control systems development. Meanwhile Nobuhiko Kawamoto had moved up to the post of Senior Managing Director of Honda, though he continued to lend advice to the Grand Prix project.

As usual engine development work was carried out at R&D's Wako base and McLaren was contracted to supply test chassis in which Emanuele Pirro would pound around the Honda-owned Suzuka circuit. Shell supplied the necessary 'rocket fuel' under an existing agreement with MI while IHI still supplied the turbos, NGK the plugs. Just about everything else was produced in house, even the pistons, rings, injectors, ignition coils and, of course, the engine management system.

In England engine preparation continued to be handled from the smart Honda facility on the Langley Business Centre close to Slough. The total number of personnel employed by Honda on its Formula One programme had grown from 60 in 1985 to 97 the following year, then to 135 with the expansion to service two teams. For 1988 the team was up to 140 members servicing around 60 2.5 bar engines. Those engines were at all times attended by 'Honda F1 Grand Prix Racing Team' personnel: one would be there, portable computer to hand even when an engine was merely fired up for a systems check at the

McLaren or Lotus factory. Every single revolution of the engine under its own power was diligently logged.

Situated in the Woking Business Park, the MI facility presented visitors with a dazzling row of seven immaculately preserved Eighties McLaren chassis, each example the most successful of its year. MI had a policy of not selling off its cars, keen to preserve the secrets of its carbon fibre composite construction. Originally the pioneering MI tubs had been assembled from parts supplied by American rocket maker Hercules but in 1984 the team installed its own autoclave and took over the moulds from Hercules, which continued to supply the materials. Pre-preg carbon fibre was kept in a special pressurised, refrigerated store to provide a reasonable shelf life.

MI had the facilities to produce virtually all parts of a Grand Prix chassis, buying in only parts such as dampers (from Showa), radiator cores (from Secan), wheels (from Dymag),gears (from X-trac and Emko), brake discs and pads (from CI) and tyres (from Goodyear - the sole supplier this season). In 1988 the company was in the process of installing a full Computer Aided Design (CAD)/ Computer Aided Machining (CAM) system, allowing the designers to work in three dimensions and to produce models and full sized moulds direct from computer generated electronic plans.

Finite Element Modelling (FEM) - stress analysis via computer models - was not yet incorporated, though had been undertaken by Hercules on the original monocoque design which had remained essentially intact. Under Barnard MI had started a rigorous lifing system for individual components. Quality control was rigorous, too, and every part produced in the factory was individually numbered, enabling all members of a rogue batch to be tracked down.

The key to chassis development in the late Eighties was aerodynamic research. Given ground effect technology it was essential to work with rolling road tunnels, though the effect of underwing activation by the exhaust could not be simulated in any tunnel. Under Murray's guidance Brabham had developed a full sized rolling road tunnel in conjunction with Southampton University but this was only suitable for lightweight mock ups and was thus only useful for

detail design work. Otherwise, the largest tunnel was the March facility which accepted 40% models and was used by Lotus. MI used the National Maritime Institute's sophisticated tunnel which could accommodate 33.3% models. In general the larger the model the greater the accuracy but the sophistication of the tunnel counted for a lot, too.

The MI facility was based at Teddington and was operated by Peter Hodgeman. Half an hour away, the MI factory employed a staff of 150 in spotlessly clean, airy surroundings and its subsidised canteen was run by three qualified chefs. It was a facility one associated with a successful computer company rather than a traditional racing team base.

Managing Director Ron Dennis had come a long way in a relatively short space of time. He had worked his way up from a hands on involvement in the sport, switching to management in the Seventies. The legacy of his practical work was an understanding of race car engineering shared by few other Team Owners. Dennis' commercial partner since the Seventies had been wealthy businessman Creighton Brown, a keen club racer. The Eighties had brought a major involvement from TAG - Techniques d'Avant-Garde - a Saudi company that had been formed in 1977 to 'institutionalize commercial activities between Europe and the Middle East', in other words to invest oil revenues.

Nevertheless, for a decade the wheels of Dennis' superbly turned out racing cars had been kept turning by Marlboro sponsorship. Early on Dennis had appreciated the importance of ensuring his operation acted as an effective marketing tool for its sponsors. That on going policy was as responsible for his long term commercial success as his race results. It was reflected in details such as a fresh coat of paint for the cars and fresh uniforms for the mechanics for each meeting. Dennis ensured MI presented the right image at all times.

It also had the right drivers in 1988, with Alain Prost joined by Ayrton Senna. Prost was arguably the best of the established aces, Senna was arguably the best of the newcomers to the elite group of multiple Grand Prix race winners. The MI Team Manager was Jo Ramirez, one time Chief Mechanic on Jo Siffert's JWA Porsche 917.

The McLaren head-
phone wearers at Rio
re (left to right), Neil
Oatley, Gordon
Murray, Ron Dennis
nd Steve Nichols.
Murray was Technical
Director, Oatley
ngineered Prost's
ar, Nichols that of
enna.

Like the few other top teams of 1988, MI had an independent test car operation clocking up miles on many of the European Grand Prix circuits away from the pressures of its race programme.

MI also had unparalleled strength in its design department with Steve Nichols - designer of the '87 MP4/3 - and Neil Oatley - designer of the '86 Cosworth/Ford-FORCE - serving under Murray. Nichols headed the team responsible for the '88 turbo car while Oatley concentrated on a normally aspirated chassis for the following season. Both could draw upon the skills of aerodynamic specialist Bob Bell and transmission specialist David North. North had been Murray's righthand man at Brabham and co-operated with Californian transmission manufacturer Pete Weismann, a man who had done much to help instigate the Brabham BT55 project.

Murray, of course, made his reputation as Brabham's designer, a job he had acquired in the early Seventies. During the '88 season he commented to Allan Staniforth: "Designing used to be such a solitary thing - all think and talk to yourself, but I don't know if there is such a thing as a racing car designer any more. I was the only one in the drawing office when I started at Brabham. Nowadays I hardly ever pick up a pencil and I have a team of 16 people. It has moved on to being a leader of a team".

Running on Empty

80 degree V6

79.0 x 50.8mm./1493.27cc.
2 IHI turbochargers
Iron block, aluminium heads
Nikasil wet aluminium liners
4 main bearings, plain
Steel crankshaft, 3 pins
Titanium con rods
Honda light alloy pistons
Honda rings
D.o.h.c., gear driven
4 valves/cylinder, 1 plug
32 degree included valve angle
Valve sizes undisclosed
Honda ignition
Honda injection
Honda engine management system
Compression ratio 9.4:1
146kg.

Regardless of engine, mid Eighties Grand Prix cars had run AP Racing's Design Council Award winning $7\frac{1}{4}$" twin plate clutch, an item carried over from the Cosworth DFV era. It was a diaphragm spring unit in which externally toothed steel pressure plates were driven by an internally toothed steel adapter ring. The adapter ring and a dished pressed steel end cover carrying the diaphragm spring were bolted to a steel flywheel which was typically no larger than the $8\frac{1}{2}$" outside diameter of the adapter ring. The flywheel and pressure plates worked in conjunction with steel driven plates onto which a bronze-based friction material was sintered. Two driven plates were rigidly attached to hubs splined to the gearbox input shaft.

AP Racing also manufactured a smaller, $5\frac{1}{2}$" plate clutch driven by six lugs rather than a toothed adapter ring. The lug drive was a little lighter, it allowed the clutch to run cooler and - its main advantage - it didn't trap dust and other debris as the clutch wore, unlike the toothed adapter ring. However, the lug driven clutch was heavily stressed where the lug joined the cover, a problem which intensified with each additional plate. A triple plate version would have been necessary to transmit Cosworth DFV, let alone turbo torque and consequently AP Racing had not developed the design for Formula One. It had not even been used in Formula Two until the early Eighties when Ron Tauranac started using a basic twin plate version in the Honda-Ralt.

The 1988 Honda RA-168-E was as low as allowed by a 5½ inch clutch and employed a unique to Formula One finger cam follower system. The drawing is of a later engine without individual cylinder butterflies.

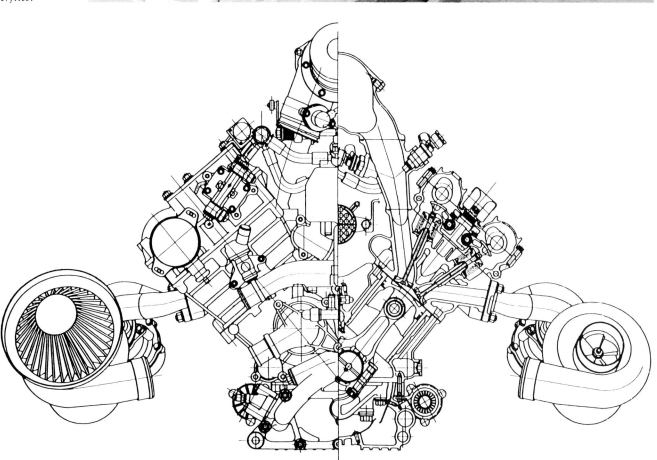

Tauranac recognised that the smaller clutch offered less mass and that its mass was concentrated nearer the centre hence there was less inertia - the main gain. In practice, the reduced inertia meant marginally superior engine response and car acceleration. Tauranac's successful use of the small clutch eventually led to Honda ordering a version for Formula One in 1987.

In the mid Eighties AP Racing started experimenting with a quadruple plate 5½" clutch running a higher spring load. By 1987 it had found that it could produce a triple plate version with a new spring and a new cover machined from a solid bar of aluminium alloy that could cope with 4.0 bar turbo torque in spite of the lug drive stresses. Honda ordered sufficient to service the 60 engines it was preparing for Williams and Lotus.

The 5½" clutch helped unlock the door to a significantly lower engine. In 1987 Honda simply replaced the conventional 7¼" clutch with the 5½" model, allowing it to switch back should the need arise. The smaller clutch worked fine and it provided considerable scope to lower the engine: the distance between the crankshaft axis and the ground could be reduced given the use of a smaller flywheel, down from 8½" (212.5mm.) in diameter to close on 6" (150mm.). Clearly this not only reduced the overall height of the engine but also beneficially reduced the centre of gravity of the 146kg. lump. In addition Honda shaved height from the top of the engine saving a total of over 2"/50mm, the overall height for '88 quoted as 627mm.

The saving from the top of the engine represented around 60% of the total gain and was made possible through the modifications required to suit the stringent new condition of 2.5 bar maximum boost. Power is a function of boost and revs and with boost limited to 4.0 bar in 1987 revs had come under the spotlight for the first time since the Formula Two days. Clearly on 2.5 bar engine speed was even more crucial and qualifying power went from 1010b.h.p. on 4.0 bar at 12,000r.p.m. to 685b.h.p. on 2.5 bar at 12,500r.p.m. Not only did higher peak power speed ensure higher power per bar boost, it called for shorter inlet tracts and thus helped lower the engine package. Certain ancillaries

were relocated with the lower package.

The jump of 500r.p.m. on 2.5 bar was not a problem in terms of mechanical stress: the RA-168-E could scream to a speed in excess of 14,000r.p.m. and survive. In qualifying the rev limiter was set at a staggering 14,000r.p.m. - probably then an all time Grand Prix record. Although there was nothing to gain in terms of output from exceeding the 12,500r.p.m. peak power speed it did offer the driver flexibility that was useful in certain circumstances. For example, on parts of the tight Hungaroring a gear could be held longer, beneficially saving shifts while keeping the turbos well spooled up.

That 14,000r.p.m. potential was in spite of the relatively high stroke:bore ratio of 0.643 which reflected a bore size compromised to the need for a short heat path from piston crown to cylinder wall. Previously, only the Renault turbo engine had breached the 13,000r.p.m. threshold. In general terms, given a cylinder capacity of only 250cc. the major problem was one of valve control rather than of mechanical stress (though not so long before the maximum piston acceleration involved would have been considered dangerously high, perhaps suicidal).

As engine speed climbs valve spring surge becomes an increasing headache. To run over 13,000r.p.m. Renault had exploited its springless pneumatic valve control and Honda was now showing the full potential of its finger cam follower system. The finger followers could be run in conjunction with very high load springs, the lack of bucket tappets offering more freedom of spring design. Twin Japanese produced helical coil springs were employed. Surge was still a limiting factor for Honda, but it clearly occurred at a higher speed than for a conventional direct operation system. The disadvantages of Honda's indirect system were in the higher camshaft location and its additional weight and complication.

The jump of 500r.p.m. in peak power speed from '87 was worth over 25 b.h.p. at 2.5 bar - a significant amount as power fell towards the 600b.h.p. level of contemporary 3.5 litre atmo engines. The loss of power highlighted the inherent problem of turbo lag. While in absolute terms cutting boost improved turbocharger response, as power fell towards the level of rival atmo engines the instant response of the latter became a stronger suit. Clearly, Honda had to strive for a competitive level of power in conjunction with enhanced driveability. Further, a massive reduction of 23% in the amount of fuel available under racing conditions called for major attention to fuel efficiency.

Valve sizes, lift and timing were unchanged from 1987. Clearly, however, both engine response and fuel efficiency could be improved through a higher compression ratio. As we have seen, the compression ratio had been increased from 7.4:1 to 8.2:1 during the course of the '87 season and for '88 it was upped significantly to 9.4:1 while retaining the 79mm. bore. That called for a re-design of the carefully shaped pent roof combustion chamber. Honda did not entertain a gap between the flat piston crown and the top of the cylinder, even at 7.4:1. Indeed, as we have seen, a squish band had been a feature of its lower compression engines and this feature was retained, together with a flat top piston: with the

Power and torque curves for the '87 and '88 engines, running 4.0 and 2.5 bar respectively. The maximum outputs in b.h.p. are 1010 and 685 respectively, higher speed and higher compression featuring in '88.

smaller chamber volume the included valve angle was reduced from 39 to 32 degrees.

Mechanically, the RA-168-E was not otherwise greatly altered from the RA-167-E that had first chased higher engine speed. The same rugged block was retained for logistical reasons, though clearly there was no longer the call for the stiffness of iron that had been such an attribute at 4.0 bar and beyond. The existing package included lightweight wet aluminium liners for good heat transfer from the piston rings to the coolant (aluminium boasts three times the rate of heat rejection of iron) while careful design and block wall thicknesses ranging from 2.0 - 3.5mm. had always helped overcome the weight penalty inherent in the use of ductile cast iron. Further, the cylinderless block was short-skirted while its heads were of aluminium alloy (A1-Si6Cu4) and its cam covers and its lower crankcase cum sump cover were of magnesium alloy.

The block was of closed deck construction while the liners were open to the coolant except

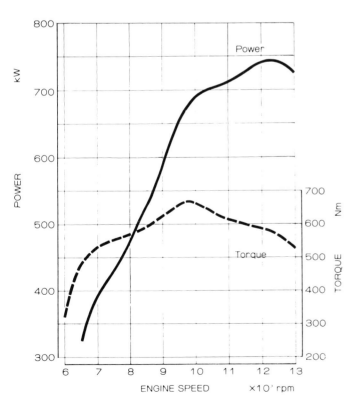

RA-167-E power characteristics

RA-168-E power characteristics

where secured at the top by a flange and where sealed at the base by two flexible O-rings, this arrangement permitting free expansion at the lower end, avoiding the problem of the differential in the expansion of aluminium and iron. The Nikasil-type liners were produced in Japan rather than by the usual supplier, Mahle in Germany. Pioneered by Mahle, nickel-silicon carbide coated aluminium liners were particularly appropriate for a turbo engine, offering excellent heat rejection characteristics while holding a tight clearance which stopped intense combustion 'torching down' a gap between piston and bore.

The piston carried three uncoated rings and was of light alloy as usual, Honda having never resorted to ceramic materials within the engine, as had oft been speculated. Oil cooling for the piston was an obvious concession to turbocharging but the method employed was not revealed. Nor were details of the valve seat material. The valves were said to be of "normal" material while the cam followers were also steel-based. Head to block sealing was via a special gasket, details of which were not disclosed.

The four main bearing caps were four bolt and as the block were of ductile cast iron. The steel crankshaft - typically nitrided for strength - ran in four plain bearings and carried plain big end bearings. Vandervell supplied its usual thin-wall shell bearings for the engine. The crankshaft was driven by I-section titanium con rods which were fitted with Honda steel gudgeon pins.

The valve angle was narrow but the valve stems were unusually long, widely spacing the cams to make room for the finger followers while leaving scope for beneficially straight downdraught inlet tracts. The latter ran down from a single central plenum with a commendably shallow angle turn at the valve seat. The basic porting had apparently come right down from the Formula Two engine. Sitting directly above the long valves - the finger followers not acting as levers in this application - the camshafts ran in four plain bearings carried directly by the head. The timing drive was taken off the front end of the crankshaft via spur gears. Two idler gears passed the drive to the camshafts. Further details of the timing drive system were not forthcoming at the time of writing since

Honda was continuing to run gear driven atmo race engines.

The front end power take-off also drove the oil and water pumps. The dry sump oil system employed a sandwich construction pump with twin engine feeds and four scavenge compartments. Each independent scavenge compartment drew lubricant through a strainer at one corner of the sump and fed it to the oil tank. Thus, the scavenge pumps effectively circulated the lubricant, which tended to gather in the sump due to longitudinal and lateral G-forces during acceleration, deceleration and cornering. As well as lubrication, the oil system played an important cooling role, heat ever the enemy of the turbo engine. Oil was pumped to the turbochargers from the main pressure pumps, returning to the crankcase for collection via the regular scavenge pumps.

Very careful attention had been paid to the development of the water cooling system, which employed two pumps, one either side of the sump. The V6 had water galleries located adjacent to the outer walls of the block and to the inner walls of each head. Each side, water was pumped into the block gallery whence it flowed over the liners and through the head, into the head gallery, this lateral flow "allowing uniform thermal conditions throughout all cylinders", according to Honda.

The RA-168-E was serviced by Honda's highly developed engine management system. Honda commented: "We attempted to design an engine management system under the concepts of "Fail Safe" and "Fail Soft". Thus, we developed a system capable of self-diagnosis and provided dual circuits for some of the sensors to improve system reliability".

The engine management system consequently featured incorporation of a Lambda probe with continuing deployment of the Honda CDI distributorless ignition. Thus, each of six centrally located NGK M10 plugs was fired by its own coil. The in house produced injection was was still known as PGMF1 and was fully electronic with sequential injection into the cylinders via two injectors. Either single or double injection could be employed, according to the quantity of fuel involved. The injectors were mounted high in the inlet tract, just below an individual butter-

Honda achieved 685b.h.p. from its 2.5 bar engine at the expense of excessive fuel consumption. Tight race fuel rationing called for warm charge air, warm fuel and a weaker mixture, factors costing power.

POWER & FUEL CONSUMPTION (F.C.) OF RA168E

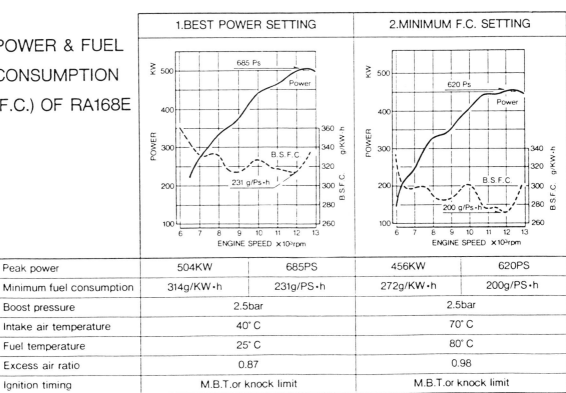

	1.BEST POWER SETTING		2.MINIMUM F.C. SETTING	
Peak power	504KW	685PS	456KW	620PS
Minimum fuel consumption	314g/KW·h	231g/PS·h	272g/KW·h	200g/PS·h
Boost pressure	2.5bar		2.5bar	
Intake air temperature	40°C		70°C	
Fuel temperature	25°C		80°C	
Excess air ratio	0.87		0.98	
Ignition timing	M.B.T.or knock limit		M.B.T.or knock limit	

fly throttle for each cylinder. Honda did not announce the injection pressure. This is likely to have been significantly higher than the 5.0 bar offered by the standard Bosch Motronic system, higher pressure improving atomisation.

Between the fuel pump and the injectors was a heat exchanger employing water from the cooling system to pre-heat the fuel, as required. This was a new development for '88 in view of the more stringent fuel ration, the effect of hot fuel again improving atomisation thus consumption, although at the expense of power. The rate of water flow into the exchanger and hence the heating effect employed at any given moment (if any) was controlled via a solenoid valve under the command of the engine management system. There was also a management system commanded solenoid valve bye-passing air from the aftercoolers as required, as seen previously.

Once again, the engine management system also governed the wastegate opening via a solenoid valve, precise boost control still an important factor in the face of the pop off valve. As we have seen, driveability was of particular concern as power fell with the cut in boost and to this end Honda sought improved transient response from its turbochargers. It switched to friction-reducing ball rather than plain bearings and lighter ceramic rather than Inconel turbine wheels. Developed by IHI, these sophisticated single stage turbochargers were known as RX6D and according to Honda, "drastically upgraded the transient properties by reducing the inertia moment and friction of revolving parts". A choice of three sizes of turbocharger was prepared for the season.

The use of ball bearings was the first major turbocharger modification since the switch to IHI, previous seasons having witnessed the gradual evolution of a conventional design with reliability the prime target. Unlike Renault and later Cosworth, still no compressor performance enhancer was used while VGS and variable turbine inlet nozzles had been long rejected as too complicated and unreliable. Neither two stage turbocharging nor compounding had featured in Honda's experimental work.

Aside from engine response, fuel chemistry, atomisation and combustion were three key problem areas affecting 2.5 bar performance.

With the higher compression ratio there was a tendency towards unstable combustion to overcome which the injector spray pattern had to be modified. The revised detailing of the combustion chamber was also important here while the increased compression ratio improved both power and fuel efficeincy for a given level of boost. However, it had only been possible given the use of toluene fuel with a very high resistance to detonation, the danger of detonation increasing with any increase in compression ratio.

Intriguingly, Honda published results of comparative tests with test fuels having toluene contents of 30%, 60% and 84%, mixing appropriate amounts of normal heptane and isooctane to achieve the required 102 (RON) octane rating. On the test bench, at 2.5 bar and 12,000r.p.m. the 84% toluene fuel permitted the ignition timing to be advanced over 10 degrees compared to the 30% mix thanks to a higher resistance to detonation. The onset of detonation was sensed through amplifying the output signal of a piezo-electric pressure transducer fixed in place of the plug washer (this device employed on the bench but never on the track). The ignition advance possible with 84% toluene fuel improved fuel consumption through higher thermal efficiency.

The striking rate of ignition timing advance possible as the toluene content increased underlines the overall importance of so called 'rocket fuel' to turbo engine development, warding off the ever present threat of detonation. As we have seen, it was toluene fuel that had opened up the path to higher boost and higher compression ratios from the typical 2.5 bar and 6.5:1 pressure levels of early Eighties pump petrol fuelled turbo engines.

Due to the greater density of toluene compared to alternative paraffine fuels, the higher the toluene content, the higher the calorific value (in effect, the higher the potential heat energy) of the fuel for a given volume. For a given weight the calorific value of the 84% toluene test fuel was marginally lower than that of the other test fuels, but FISA restricted fuel by volume, not weight. For a given volume the heaviest, 84% toluene brew offered considerably enhanced consumption over the lower level mixes.

The disadvantage of the 84% mix was poorer atomisation, as is indicated by an initial boiling

ENGINE MANAGEMENT SYSTEMS FOR RA168E

This simplified engine management diagram for the RA-168-E omits the Lambda probe, an essential feature since it offered a self diagnosis facility. The system sent telemetry signals to the pits as seen below.

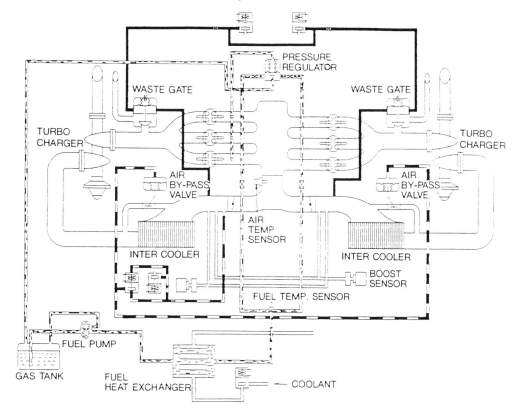

BOOST CONTROL SYSTEM

INTAKE AIR TEMPERATURE CONTROL SYSTEM

FUEL TEMPERATURE CONTROL SYSTEM

point of 100, compared to 96 for the 30% mix. The 30% mix was comprised of 66% isooctane and 4% n-Heptane and had a RON octane rating of 101.6, a density of 0.747, a net calorific value of 10,300 Kcal./Kg. and a stoichiometric ratio of 14.5:1. By way of comparison, the 84% mix comprised 16% n-Heptane and had a RON of 101.8, a density of 0.84 a net calorific value of 9,817 Kcal./Kg. and a stoichiometric ratio of 13.7.

Running the RA-168-E on the 84% toluene mix with an air ratio of 1.15 (compared to 1.23 for the '87 7.4:1 compression ratio, 4.0 bar engine) Honda announced its qualifying output as 685b.h.p. together with torque of 43.2kg.m. At 2.5 bar the RA-168-E in qualifying configuration produced marginally higher power than the RA-167-E given the same boost level due to its higher speed and compression ratio. To achieve the 685b.h.p. output the charge air temperature was cooled to the regular level of 40 degrees centigrade and this condition plus the 15% rich 'high power' mixture produced unacceptably high fuel consumption for a 150 litre race engine.

From logging ECU sensor readings Honda had discovered that full and closed throttle conditions dominated race driving and thus concentrated upon improving fuel consumption at full throttle. Interestingly, as boost was increased from 2.2 to 2.5 bar both power output and fuel consumption registered improvement. Honda attributed this phenomenon to improved charging efficiency leading to improved thermal efficiency.

To obtain the best fuel consumption at 2.5 bar Honda found it necessary to run a charge air temperature of 70 degrees centigrade and a weak mixture - an air ratio of 1.02 - and a fuel temperature of 80 degrees centigrade. Under these conditions Honda was able to produce an extremely frugal race engine having a brake specific fuel consumption (BSFC) of 200 gms./b.h.p./hr. at 12,000r.p.m. and giving maximum power of 620b.h.p. at 12,500r.p.m. Compared to the maximum power settings, fuel consumption was improved by no less than 13%.

The maximum power and maximum economy settings made little difference to the power curve up to 8,000r.p.m. Then the economy engine's curve flattened out, the 13% gain in fuel econ-

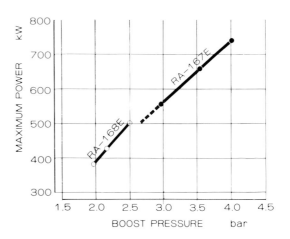

Maximum power of RA-168-E and RA-167-E related to boost pressure

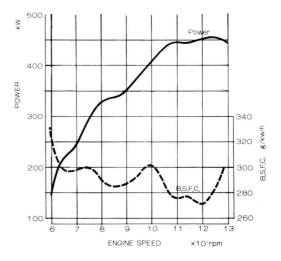

RA-168-E performance at minimum fuel consumption

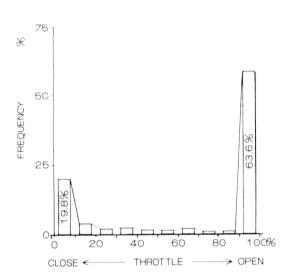

**Throttle opening distribution during
a race event ('88 San Marino GP)**

		A	B	RACING FUEL
Fuel ingredient	Toluene (%)	30	60	84
	n-Heptane (%)	4	9.5	16
	Isooctane (%)	66	30.5	0
Research Octane Number		101.6	101.9	101.8
Motor Octane Number		94.2	91.2	90.0
Density (at 15°C)		0.747	0.799	0.840
Net Calorific Value (Kcal/Kg)		10300	10015	9817
Stoichiometric Ratio		14.5	14.0	13.7
Reid Vapor Pressure (Kg/cm²)		0.154	0.141	0.120
Initial Boiling Point (°C)		96.0	98.5	100.0
10% (°C)		97.5	100.5	105.0
50% (°C)		98.5	102.0	106.0
90% (°C)		100.0	105.0	108.0
End Point (°C)		123.5	108.0	116.0

Test fuel specifications

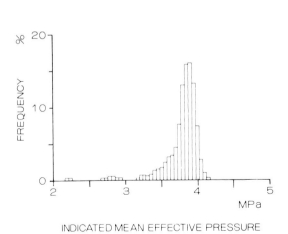

I.M.E.P. frequency distribution

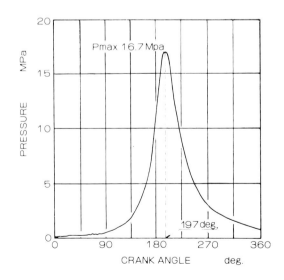

**Cylinder pressure diagram of RA-168-E under
condition of maximum power generation**

omy won at the cost of 9.5% power.

Higher r.p.m., a lower air intake temperature and a richer mixture all improved power and were factors that could be varied by the driver during the course of a race. Thus, he had a very flexible response available to his fuel situation. As we have seen, the air intake temperature was controlled via an aftercooler bye-pass. Directing all the charge air through the aftercoolers reduced its temperature down to 40 degrees centigrade (assuming an ambient temperature in the region of 25 degrees). The bye-pass valve could be opened progressively to increase the charge temperature and power and BSFC both fell steadily as the temperature rose. At 70 degrees the improvement in fuel consumption reached saturation point, though the fall in power was not checked.

The progressive improvement in BSFC as charge temperature rose from 40 to 70 degrees could be attributed to improved atomisation. Toluene based fuel was not easily atomised at low temperature, thriving on high boost and the associated high engine temperatures. The fall in power was mainly attributable to necessarily retarded ignition, the charge air temperature increase increasing the engine's susceptibility to detonation. Retarding the ignition too far had a negative effect on BSFC as well as power, causing reduced thermal efficiency.

Improved atomisation was also achieved through pre-heating the fuel via the aforementioned heat exchanger. It was possible to heat the fuel to a temperature 15 degrees below that of the water. The amount of water flowing into the exchanger was controlled by a solenoid valve, this maintaining the desired fuel temperature. Fuel consumption improved as the fuel temperature was increased from 40 to 80 degrees, beyond which the effect was saturated. Power fell marginally with the increased fuel temperature, and continued falling if the temperature rose beyond 80 degrees.

The fuel:air ratio predictably improved consumption and decreased power as it was weakened off. It was possible to achieve further gains in consumption by weakening the mixture below the ratio of 1.02 but at the expense of unsatisfactory transient response: the engine "became insufficient for racing performance", as Honda

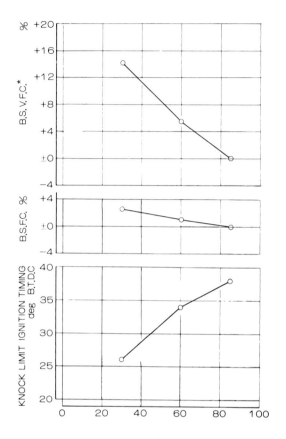

Effect of toluene content ratio on knock limit ignition timing and fuel consumption

* **B.S.V.F.C. "brake specific volumetric fuel consumption" (cc/kwh)**

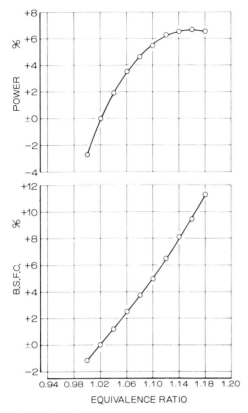

Effect of equivalence ratio on power and B.S.F.C.

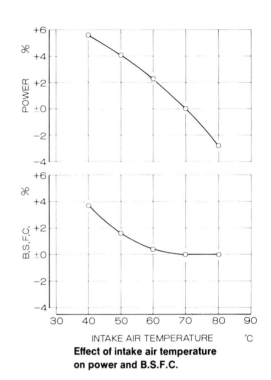

**Effect of intake air temperature
on power and B.S.F.C.**

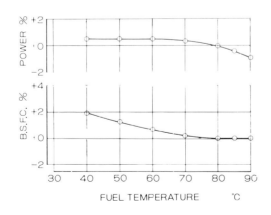

Effect of fuel temperature on power and B.S.F.C.

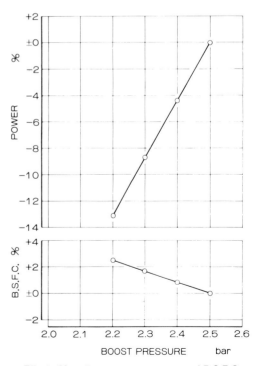

Effect of boost pressure on power and B.S.F.C.

put it. As the mixture was richened from 1.02 power increased until the ratio of 1.15 was achieved, at which point it peaked. It was at 1.15 and running a 40 degree charge temperature the RA-168-E gave its impressive 685b.h.p. at 12,500r.p.m. - 183b.h.p. per litre per bar boost.

That qualifying output was achieved with a standard 9.4:1 compression ratio engine - as usual, Honda did not alter the mechanical specification for qualifying. The 1988 engine was known in full as the RA-168-E-XE1.

Low Life

MI/ Hercules carbon fibre composite **monocoque**
Stressed engine
Pullrod front suspension, pushrod rear
Showa dampers
Dymag magnesium 13" rims
CI 11" carbon-carbon discs, outboard
MI twin, two pot calipers, CI pads
Carbon fibre bodywork
2 Secan water radiators, 2 Secan oil heat exchangers
2 Secan air:air aftercoolers
AP 5½" twin plate clutch
MI six speed gearbox
Torsen l.s.d.
150 litre ATL fuel tank, 9 litre oil tank
Gates battery, Honda instruments
2875mm. wheelbase; 1824mm. front track, 1670mm. rear
540kg.

The MP4/4 marked a complete break from the evolutionary line of Porsche/TAG turbocars descended from John Barnard's original Cosworth DFV design for Project Four. Both the monocoque and the transaxle were brand new, replacing items inherited from the original Cosworth-powered MP4, while the aerodynamic package also broke with tradition thanks to the arrival of Murray. The new conditions allowed smaller coolers and required a smaller fuel tank. Further, as we have seen, Honda lowered its engine significantly and Murray's influence ensured that the all new MP4/4 was the son of his illfated BT55, with the same fuselage height and exactly the same driving position.

As we have noted, Murray had arrived at Woking too late to influence the MP4/3, which was a committee-designed evolution of Barnard's long standing design, retaining the regular monocoque and transaxle. Murray felt neither item to be adequate. The monocoque had been drawn for a full ground effect car and was therefore narrow: its lack of cross-sectional area clearly cost rigidity, as did a riveted-in aluminium front bulkhead assembly (the legacy of 1981 rocker arm front suspension). The transaxle was even older, harking back to the Seventies - its design had been bought from Tyrrell. Murray found it "way out of date" and somewhat delicate while complex load paths from the rear suspension represented yet another obvious structural weakness.

Murray says that the torsional rigidity of the time honoured monocoque had not been measured for years. He produced a rig test and while unwilling to quote actual figures will admit that he found the MP4/3's axle to axle rigidity only 50% of that of the Brabham BT55, which he had considered merely "adequate for the period" (and certainly not the ultimate attainable). A low line design would require new monocoque and there was clearly a need for it. Further, the lower Honda engine called for a revised layout transaxle (or upward angled powertrain) to avoid lowering the c.w.p. which was already sitting below the wheel hubs, putting the driveshafts through an unhealthy working angle.

Murray confirms that he strongly believed in the BT55 philosophy, consequently even before Honda arrived on the scene he had started looking at the potential for a lower McLaren package. He found that with the compact Porsche/ TAG engine he could produce a half way stage between the MP4/3 and the BT55. However, with Goto's lower RA-168-E Murray found he could reproduce the actual BT55 seating position, keeping bevelled upper cockpit and fuel tank flanks in line with the cam covers. Consequently the MP4/4 retained the BT55 seat and leg angles and its steering wheel position, well proven from a control point of view.

Prost did not take enthusiastically to the head down, laid back driving position when he tried a wooden mock up in the summer of '87. The value of enhanced airflow to the rear wing was great enough to force him to accept its desirability. An annual improvement in aerodynamic efficiency of 2% represented a very good step: Murray reports that the BT55-style MP4/4 package provided a staggering 6% improvement over the MP4/3.

The necessary new monocoque had a greater cross-sectional area and an all carbon front end which helped MI to more than double its axle to axle torsional rigidity figure. To step up the drive from the low clutch to a c.w.p. at an ideal height Murray devised a three-shaft transmission within an appropriately stiffer casing. Otherwise, the MP4/4 was a very simple car, as Murray remarked to Racecar Engineering contributor Allan Staniforth at the time. He observed: "Chapman laid the driver right back, its not a new idea, and drivers will never sit right up again. The MP4/4 is very low, it has a low frontal area and a lot of good flow to the rear wing. It is a simple basic design, particularly at the front where everyone has got very complicated on suspension".

Overall, the MP4/4 was far less unconventional than the BT55 thanks to a number of factors. The MP4/4 carried a straightforward combination of upright V6 engine and symmetrical transaxle and consequently had a shorter wheelbase (albeit one of the longest of the '88 crop) as well as a more conventional rear shroud and underwing than the radical BT55. Further, its 2.5 bar engine made lighter cooling demands and could drink no more than 150 litres.

Two regulation changes heavily influenced turbocar design for 1988: the reduction of the maximum fuel tank size volume from 195 to 150 litres and the stipulation that the driver's feet be located behind the front wheel axis. The smaller tank clearly assisted Murray's quest to get everything as low as possible within a regular wheelbase length whereas the pedal position ruling worked in the opposite direction. Moving the pedals back led some designers - particularly those of atmo cars with larger fuel tanks - towards a shorter bellhousing and even caused side extensions of 200-plus litre central tanks.

After the unhappy experience of the BT55 Murray sought not only tighter control on the length of the wheelbase but within that constraint a traditional 40 - 60 front - rear weight distribution percentage split which called for a conventional engine to c.w.p. distance. The V6 turbo engine's multi cooler requirement ruled out a tank wider than the tub base while for aerodynamic reasons the tank had to be kept to cam cover height and consequently was of a given length. Ultimately the length of the wheelbase was determined by the size of drivers Prost and the slightly taller Senna in the new seating position. Both drivers were beneficially pint sized, a lanky driver would have presented a real problem.

Compared to the MP4/3 of 1987, the pedals were 200mm. further back to suit the revised regulations but the 45 litre smaller fuel tank was significantly shorter to the extent that the wheelbase was only 40mm. longer in spite of the heavily reclined driving position. In effect, the driver moved back into what formally had been fuel tank space and with the shorter tank the important distance from the roll bar to the leading edge of the rear wing was unavoidably shorter. Nevertheless, the MP4/4 had its centre of gravity in the ideal location - within the fuel tank region - while the overall-improved aerodynamic package put its centre of pressure in the right place, a little way in front of the centre of gravity.

Thus, the MP4/4 had the right engine package and the right fuel tank size with which to fully exploit the low line car philosophy. Its all new chassis represented a considerable investment by MI for just one season and the new partnership with Honda made for "an explosion of work load", Murray reflects. He had to oversee an interim MP4/3 for off season Honda engine testing as well as the MP4/4, and to plan for the V10 programme due to start track testing well ahead of the '89 season. The drawing office staff duly increased while the various projects were split up with Steve Nichols heading the MP4/4 design team.

The brand new monocoque was drawn by Matthew Jeffreys with Mike Lock re-doing the tooling. Most late Eighties monocoques were made by laying up inside a female tool, this technique allowing compound curves to be formed and leaving a smooth external skin which together gave the designer the option to dispense with conventional bodywork. However, to allow access for lay up and to allow the product to be removed from the tooling after curing it generally had to be formed as two major pieces, leaving a seam belt as a potential source of weakness.

With the BT55 Murray had produced the first ever seamless monocoque in female tooling. He left the front and rear bulkheads out and sent someone inside on a trolley to lay-up what was effectively an open ended tube. Barnard's MI monocoque had always been seamless and it had integral front and rear bulkheads. Its lay up was done around a male tool cut vertically into a number of bolt-together sections. During lay up and curing a bolt running end to end held the assembly together. Unbolted, the tool could be removed one section at a time through the cockpit opening.

One drawback of the MI monocoque was a larger than ideal cockpit opening, another was a lack of freedom for aerodynamic sculpturing. Retaining MI's usual method of construction, the MP4/4 tub was of traditional angular form and consequently was almost completely enclosed, carbon fibre bodywork exposing only its

slab sides ahead of the sidepod inlets. However, since the MI tub had its smooth surface on the inside it was easier to fit the internal bulkheads; overall it was a straightforward proposition structurally.

The MI monocoque was also unusual in being skinned purely in carbon fibre, rather than in a combination of graphite filaments and the Du Pont corporation's aramid fibre known as Kevlar. Hot cured epoxy resin can be combined with fibres of either carbon (graphite) or Kevlar to produce the skin of a high performance pressure bonded composite material, with the choice generally of aluminium or Nomex honeycomb for the core. Carbon fibre offers greater stiffness than Kevlar while Kevlar is cheaper and more resistant to tear. The two materials were typically combined with a view to maximum impact resistance.

MI's experience since 1980 included a number of convincing crash tests of its all-carbon tub. The MP4/4 tub again consisted only of carbon fibre skins, with aluminium honeycomb for the core, this machined down in areas where less strength was required. The carbon fibres were new, higher strength offering from Hercules and were unidirectional rather than woven, following Barnard's long standing prescription. The new fibre, a new resin, revised lay up and layering together with the lack of the old aluminium front bulkhead assembly helped achieve a decrease in weight along with an increase in stiffness.

The lighter MP4/4 tub contained four internal bulkheads, two spring/damper boxes and two inner panels, all these items bonded into the main male-tooled, autoclave baked moulding. They were of similar composite construction. Set between the damper boxes, the pedals were bracketed to the floor. Further back, the battery was located on the floor just behind the dash bulkhead. Immediately ahead, similarly tucked under the driver's legs, was the fire extinguisher. The mandatory 5.0 and 2.5 kilogramme bottles were combined in a specially shaped floor mounted pod. This was produced by Lifeline to McLaren drawings. The driver sat in an individually tailored carbon fibre seat, strapped in via Willans belts.

The monocoque inner panels and damper boxes

The MP4/4 monocoque (overleaf) was a seamless carbon fibre over aluminium honeycomb production using materials provided by Hercules, the American rocket maker. The crash-tested nose box was of similar construction.

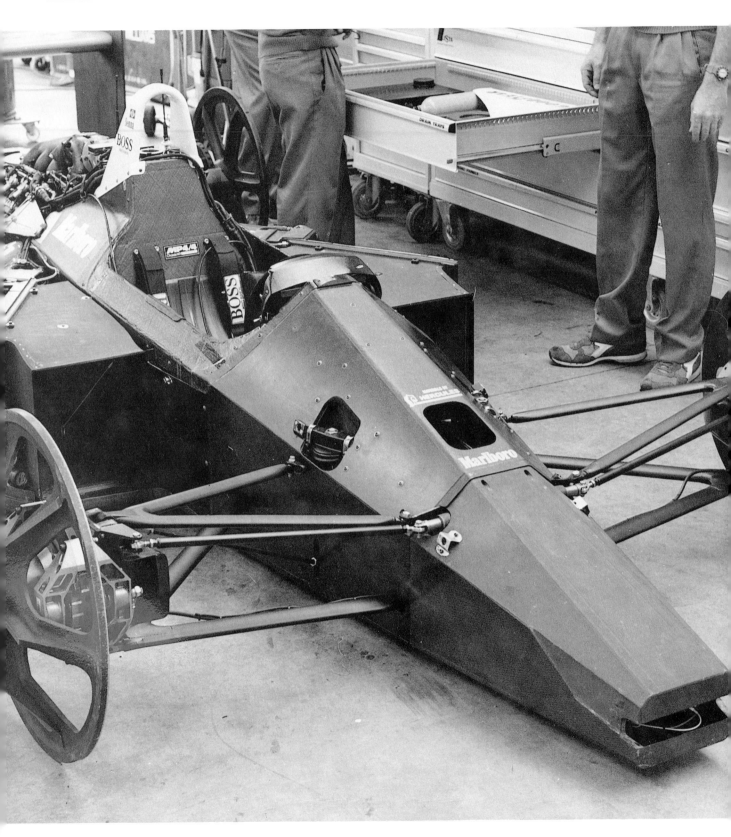

formed box-sections running the length of the cockpit either side of the driver. Such box sections were required by the regulations but added little to torsional rigidity and thus were often overlooked by other teams. Since FISA was allowing such oversights it was proposing to drop the box section requirement. However, Murray was against that, pointing to the fact that Formula One shunts are rarely head on. In the event of an angled impact box sections would help stop a tub splitting asunder.

The inserted MP4/4 bulkheads sat at the front of the tank, at the dash and back and front of the damper boxes. Those forward bulkheads supported the anti roll bar and the forward steering column bearing respectively, the steering rack bolting to the front of the tub. The rack ran in a new casting designed to bolt directly to the front bulkhead, whereas the MP4/3 rack had been bracketed. This modification was a Brabham-proven recipe to improve steering feel in high speed corners, one of the problem areas for the '87 Porsche/TAG-McLaren.

The front suspension was carried by the forward portion of the tub with loads fed into it at the damper box and dash bulkheads. Ahead was a mandatory crash-tested nose box, again of carbon fibre over aluminium honeycomb. Bonded to the front bulkhead, it carried the front wings. The forward safety roll hoop was an aluminium production bolted to the top of the dash bulkhead while the rear hoop was steel and was afixed to the top of the tank. The main engine management system box sat atop the tank with other boxes located in the pods, above the coolers.

The sidepod mounted coolers were attached to the tub via fully stressed carbon fibre composite ducting, the radiator sitting in its own duct which was screwed to the side of the tub while the aftercooler behind it was additionally supported by a tube fixed to the engine, this tube in turn helping support the pod floor. The pod undertrays were formed as part of a fully detachable underwing. The single piece underwing was carbon over aluminium honeycomb, except where it was liable to rub the track. There Kevlar skinning was used for its greater resistance to tear. The front and rear wings were formed of carbon fibre over Nomex honeycomb.

The new Honda engine bolted to the back of the tub via Cosworth-style cam cover and sump pick ups and its transaxle carried the rear suspension, the central post mounted wing and the rear portion of the underwing. The oil tank was formed integrally with the bellhousing. The rear diffuser upsweep was assisted by the new three-shaft transmission package, along with the driveshaft working angle. MI's expensive new transaxle was sketched out by Murray who subsequently brought in two long term associates, David North and Pete Weismann. Former Brabham design assistant North drew the transaxle and the rear suspension while Weismann continued to act as a transmission consultant for Murray, a role he had played since 1971.

MI's new transaxle was fed by a choice of conventional or carbon-carbon 5 ½" clutch. The latter was essentially the '87 lug driven clutch fitted with carbon-carbon pressure and drive plates. The same material as employed for carbon-carbon brake discs was used to produce a significantly lighter clutch offering even less mass, even less inertia and saving further weight from the flywheel which could be aluminium rather than steel. Further, the carbon-carbon clutch could be slipped intentionally without damage, released cleanly and instantly and offered a good wear rate. The AP Racing carbon-carbon clutch employed material supplied by the French Carbone Industrie (CI) concern whereas AP Racing carbon-carbon discs were manufactured by CI rival Hitco in the USA.

The clutch shaft fed under the c.w.p. into the base of the gearbox where the drive was stepped up to the two usual gear shafts via a variable primary ratio. As usual, the drive went forward from the upper gear shaft to the pinion. The gearbox was of the non-syncromesh Hewland pattern and had a conventional gear change mechanism rather than the clever quick-shift mechanism devised by Weismann which had been employed by the BT55. Due to lack of time North incorporated a modified Hewland shift system. The box was equipped with gears produced by X-Trac in the UK and Emko in the USA and was dry sump, unlike the MP4/3 box.

Murray had studied the MP4/3 gearbox via data logging and rig tests and had found to his horror a complete lack of oil pressure under braking. Hence the new dry rather than wet sump oiling system. A three litre oil tank was duly incorporated in the bellhousing section of the new transaxle casing, right behind the nine litre engine oil tank. The entire clutch, gearbox and final drive was contained within the new bespoke magnesium casting which provide structurally improved mounts for the rear suspension. The MP4/4 case was lighter and stiffer than the item it replaced, and it provided better bearing support. It split into front and rear sections along the rear wheel axis for access to the differential.

The final drive was via a Torsen differential. MI had regularly run a Torsen differential since 1984. Produced by the Gleason Gear Works of Rochester, New York, the Torsen ('Torque Sensing') differential exploited the principle that a worm can drive a wheel but a wheel cannot drive a worm to bias torque. With its smooth operation it was claimed to improve handling and traction, particularly in the wet. However, it was heavy and had small gears relative to the amount of torque it was asked to handle and thus it had needed a lot of development work by MI - which had an exclusive deal with Gleason - to make it suitable for Formula One. Over the years MI had made it very reliable and had modified its operation to suit its needs.

Steel driveshafts were employed with MI-design c.v. joints both ends and the outer c.v. joint was integrated with the hub, into which the outer bearing track was machined. This Barnard innovation made for a lighter, more rigid assembly and kept the c.v. joint hidden within the upright assembly. The hub cum stub axle was of high grade steel and both front and rear ran in twin SKF roller bearings carried directly by the upright. The front stub axle was retained by a large nut on the inside of the upright.

The MP4/4 featured a pullrod front suspension system, a pushrod rear, the concept of tension and compression links having been pioneered in Formula One by Murray on the Brabham BT44 of the mid Seventies. Prior to that spring/damper units had been either mounted outboard compressed by stout lower wishbones or inboard worked by beefy rocker arms. Murray's solution, originally thought up for a personal 750 Formula project he had never found time to

complete, was lighter and was structurally and aerodynamically more efficient.

The MP4/4 set its dampers upright, either side of the pedals, either side of the transaxle. Its pullrod front suspension system featured the use of novel 'roller tracks' as seen on North's '87 BT56 design and before that Murray's BT48. With this arrangement the pullrod acted directly upon a pin at the base of the spring/damper unit, this pin following a curved track which described an arc similar to that which would be traced by the usual inboard rocker arm. The roller track was more economical on space, which was at a premium in the front of the chisel-nosed MP4/4 monocoque. Further, the track eliminated the high point loading of a rocker near the centre of the tub, feeding the loading instead into the adjacent outer wall of the structure. Additionally, the designer was not tied to a natural arc as described by a rocker arm.

The dampers were supplied by Showa, a Honda sponsor which replaced Bilstein. MI had enjoyed a good relationship with Bilstein but saw an excellent opportunity to work more closely with Showa, on an exclusive basis. Showa supplied oil/gas dampers with remote cylinders which offered a tremedous range of adjustment for individual tracks. They also offered the facility of cockpit adjustment for bump only through three settings - hard, medium, soft.

The front lower wishbone was wide based, its rear leg picking up at the level of the dash bulkhead. The upper wishbone was much narrower in base and both linkages were steel carrying steel uprights. The suspension links fed their loads into the tub via aluminium brackets while the roller tracks were titanium and carried roller bearings. The steering arms ran ahead of the upper wishbone since the rack was mounted on the front of the tub.

Produced by Jack Knight, the rack provided a 9:1 steering ratio as standard. The front suspension geometry was carefully adapted at the design stage to avoid the need for an ear on the nose panel to fair-in upper wishbone mounts. At the rear the spring/damper units standing upright either side of the transaxle were operated through the usual combination of pushrod and compact rocker. Upper and lower wishbones were employed, with a lower mounted track control

New for '88: a
transaxle containing a
dry sump three shaft
gearbox. The gearbox oil
tank was tucked behind
the engine oil tank, the
latter in the bellhousing.
The magnesium case
splits transversely for
c.w.p. access.

arm. A short titanium anti roll bar was employed both front and rear.

The hubs drove the wheels and the brake bells via three steel pegs at the front, six at the rear. The brake bells were aluminium carrying carbon-carbon discs, 11" in diameter and 0.9" thick. Due to lack of time the MP4/4 was somewhat over-braked, it brakes drawn from the existing MI equipment which had been developed for high boost turbocar application. The basic specification was ventilated CI carbon-carbon discs, in house bells and in house twin two pot calipers.

MI had worked with CI since the advent of carbon fibre reinforced carbon discs in the early Eighties. Carbon-carbon discs running in conjunction with carbon pads offered greater deceleration yet lower pedal effort than traditional cast iron brakes but in the face of far higher operating temperatures the challenge had been one of heat dissipation, particularly on slow, heavy braking circuits. Careful ducting of cooling air and disc and caliper development had all played important roles in making carbon-carbon brakes effective everywhere.

There were only two suppliers of carbon-carbon discs, CI and AP Racing, the latter offering discs produced by Hitco. The two manufacturers' discs had slightly different characteristics, Hitco's having a higher co-efficient of friction cold and increasing its co-efficient more gently, albeit to a marginally lower level than the CI disc. During 1987 CI had introduced a disc roughly 0.9" (in fact, 23mm.) rather than 1.0" (25.mm.) thick for less mass in an attempt to steady the rate of temperature rise and cooling.

The discs were all of 11"/279mm. diameter since that was the largest size that could be squeezed within the 13"/330mm. diameter rim that was required to carry the standard Goodyear tyre. Keeping the brake inside the rim was essential from the point of view of aerodynamics but made cooling a greater challenge.

Late Eighties caliper design had to reflect the higher heat generated running carbon-carbon discs. For example, magnesium calipers could not be employed in conjunction with carbon-carbon discs since caliper body temperature was liable to exceed 300 degrees centigrade, the point at which magnesium loses strength. De-

signed under Barnard, MI's calipers were machined from a solid forged billet of aluminium alloy to enable use of the highest possible grade material and were of a complex design with aluminium cylinders and a titanium bridge. They incorporated some clever ideas to protect against heat, including a finned piston end to help lower the temperature of the fluid.

The majority of teams ran AP or Brembo single four pot aluminium calipers whereas MI traditionally employed twin two pot calipers, one on either side of the disc. The twin two pot system was heavier but offered a greater surface area, the better to dissipate heat. Further, since it gripped the disc both sides it put less strain on the wheel bearing and a smaller bearing could be employed. However, given 1988 requirements, the MI system was heavy, over-complex and unnecessarily difficult to cool. Had he enjoyed sufficient time, Murray would have introduced a simpler braking system.

In any event, an adequate supply of brake cooling air called for careful ducting in through the upright and out through the wheel. Further, cooling air was required for the wheelbearings as well as the discs. MI ran Dymag one piece magnesium wheels, 11.5" wide at the front, 16.5" wide at the rear and produced to its own design.

Of course, this season everyone started equal in terms of footwear thanks to the universal use of Goodyear's radial tyres. Tyre performance is a vital factor in car competitiveness. The single supplier situation effectively ruled out the use of short life qualifying specials and throughout each meeting everyone would start on an equal footing in 1988, as had been the case in 1987. In 1987 qualifying and race records had fallen in spite of a 4.0 bar limit and the supply of standard rubber by Goodyear. No longer had favoured teams benefited from tyre company support - it had been up to each engineer to make the most of the same potential.

While suspension design and development played an important role in that quest, the overriding consideration as ever was aerodynamic performance - specifically, the amount of downforce generated and its cost in terms of induced drag. Drag was of particular concern for MI given the emphasis upon fuel efficiency - all Honda's efforts would have been wasted given an aerodynamically inefficient chassis. In this respect the 6% gain in aerodynamic efficiency from the low line fuselage was particularly significant.

The MP4/4's aerodynamic form was determined by four distinct elements, all of course working together within the total aerodynamic package: the front wing, the fuselage shroud, the underwing and the rear wing. The car was inevitably designed to run low and steel skid plates were fitted at the front of the tub (one at each corner) and at the base of the transaxle. However, Murray's philosophy, as that of Barnard before him, was not to run as low as physically possible.

To get the ultimate performance from the underwing it was necessary to run with an absolute minimum of wheel movement. No droop front suspension with 1000lb. springs pre-loaded by 1000lbs. would keep a car rock solid at lower speeds and under no circumstances able to lift the front of its underwing above static ride height, provided the driver kept off the kerbs. Should he have the misfortune to hit a kerb at an awkward angle, thanks to the lack of wheel movement the result could be disastrous. Further, his stiffly sprung track hugging device was difficult to control over bumps and uncomfortable to drive.

Both Murray and Barnard preferred to run with more wheel movement, movement through bump and droop. Murray admits that this cost something in terms of downforce while more pitch change made the location of the centre of pressure more difficult to control. On the other hand, a track hugging car producing more downforce per square inch from its underwing was more sensitive to any change in pitch.

The MP4/4 was designed to run sub-1000lb. front springs without any pre-load. Thus, it was softly sprung by 1988 Formula One standards, though its ride height was low compared to that run by MI back in 1983, the first year of flat bottoms. No restriction was placed on droop while a fixed measure of anti-dive and anti-squat (not 100%) was designed into the suspension geometry to help minimise pitch changes.

Right from the outset the MP4/4 aerodynamic package was designed to work effectively given proper wheel movement, following the tradi-tional Barnard approach. Other designers preferred the track hugging solid suspension route, producing an inevitably more twitchy car that would have to be fought over bumps. Given the alternative driver friendly philosophy held by both Barnard and Murray, the higher ride height MP4/4 did not necessarily employ every possible means of discouraging air flowing to the under body region.

The MP4/4's front wing was a straightforward design and was single piece, its main beam section passing through a cut out in the nose box, to which it was secured. Thus, the main elements visible either side of the nose cone were fixed. Each was equipped with an adjustable single slotted flap at the trailing edge and a pronounced triangular endplate. The front wing spanned the width of the car between the front wheels and its endplates were taken back close to the tyre. They were fitted with Jaybrook wood/fibre skirts to run as closely as possible to the ground.

The rear wing was three element, carrying twin slotted flaps, the upper flap run at a very steep angle and fitted with a Gurney lip. That is the classic recipe for a high downforce single seater rear wing. The MP4/4 wing had deep endplates, these reaching down to suspension height. A short gap between the top of the diffuser upsweep and the bottom of the endplate was bridged by a tie extending down from the endplate. The wing's central post was formed as twin plates which were bolted to the rear of the transaxle case.

The underwing was superficially of familiar Barnard McLaren form incorporating the pod floors and extending close to the rear wheels with sealing plates outside the pod plan area. Linking the two pods, it concealed the floor of the tub from a line level with the pod inlets. Where the large detachable underwing was concealed by the sidepod it had rounded-off rather than sharp edges. The diffuser upsweep started right at the rear wheels. It was cleared by the suspension and transaxle and it extended back under the rear wing but not right to the limit of rear overhang, unlike the wing. In elevation, it featured a reflex-style compound curve route following a suggestion by North whereas the Barnard cars had run a more direct upsweep.

The wing logically extended back as far as was permitted by the regulations. Ideally a rear wing is cantilevered behind the rear axle to set it in as clean air as possible and to provide additional leverage and Eighties regulations restricted rear overhang in the interest of curbing downforce. Clearly, the MP4/4's underwing and the transaxle cowl stopped short at the rear wing's central post in respect of the crucial wing/underwing interaction.

The rear wing scavenged diffuser was fitted with longitudinal guide plates which ran directly below the sides of a transaxle cowl of engine width. The exhausts discharged into the diffuser within the confines of these guide plates, each bank's system 'blowing' its own side. Outside the width of the transaxle shroud the upper surface of the diffuser upsweep was, of course, exposed, creating another aerodynamic surface.

The rear of the fuselage featured the characteristic MP4 'Coke bottle' planform that was known to work well with a diffuser. However, there was, of course, no sign of the bubble-shaped dorsum that had been another of Barnard's hallmarks. Instead there was a skinny fuel tank top/plenum cowl that was effectively an extension of the heavily reclined driver's headrest, being lower and marginally slimmer than his helmet. Beneath the fuselage shroud flared to hug the low set cam covers. Ahead of that it extended to form low cockpit sides at the same level and the same angle, the driver's low set shoulders keeping within the engine's frontal area.

The fuselage shroud fitted closely to the chisel-fronted monocoque. The MP4/4's nose section was markedly narrower than that of the MP4/3 and blended smoothly into the scuttle cover. The latter fronted a one-piece detachable cowling for the rest of the chassis, this flaring to form the sidepod covers and extending right back to the rear wing post. It incorporated a plastic windscreen. Thanks to side venting the tops of the pods were flat, and they extended back into a flat rear deck on the same level and concealing the transaxle. Only the sides of the transaxle shroud were detachable from the integral cockpit, pod and drivetrain cowl.

The water radiators and aftercoolers were bespoke items, produced in house from Secan cores. Secan oil heat exchangers were plumbed into the water system. Both air activated coolers were mounted upright and at an angle across the pod tunnel. Lying ahead of the aftercooler the radiator vented out through the side of the pod. Its leading edge touched the outer wall of the pod tunnel but a gap was left between its inner edge and the inner wall (against the side of the monocoque). This gap fed air to the aftercooler which vented out through the engine width transaxle shroud, the hot air passing over the turbocharger and exhaust system which somehow squeezed inside the pronounced 'Coke bottle' plan. The compressors faced forwards and were fed by periscope scoops which projected through the lids of the sidepods.

Honda had an optional memory box to collect engine information and provision was made for this at the base of the left hand pod. To cool it, air was ducted in through a small adjacent scoop. The fuel system included a Bendix electric pump which cut out once the engine was firing, a mechanical pump taking over. Inside the fuel cell four small scavenge pumps fed a central collector pot, from which the main pump drew.

The car was right on the 540kg. weight limit. Indeed, it required ballasting from a dry weight of around 534kg. The ballast was set in the pod floors, either side of the fuel tank and thus at the centre of gravity.

Blockbuster

yrton Senna at Rio,
ening round of the
'88 World
iampionship. The new
o line McLaren lacked
ting yet was fully in
arge. Already Ferrari
t overshadowed in the
wer stakes, while
tus was floundering.

Ayrton Senna's first World Championship title was not unexpected. Over a period of five years Senna had steadily emerged as a genius to rival Prost, winner of more Grands Prix than any other driver. Meanwhile, '87 World Champion Piquet's star was on the wane. Honda, of course, had all three acknowledged aces in its hand. Ferrari had Berger, the atmo ranks included Mansell. But the combination of Prost and Senna made for by far the strongest force in the '88 field. That helped make the most of the best car. The skill of Senna and Prost was matched by MI's almost flawless team management while

for 1988 both Honda and MI had made significant technical strides ahead the opposition. How well it showed on the track.

Honda shrugged off Ferrari's rival V6 turbo and the traditional V8 atmo engines as it ran the RA-168-E to a previously uncharted region of Formula One engine speed, achieving a record level of b.h.p. per litre per bar boost which was complemented by a major leap in Formula One race winning fuel efficiency. Significantly, the figure of b.h.p. per litre per bar boost - just over 180 - was higher than the best b.h.p. per litre ever achieved by an atmospheric Formula One en-

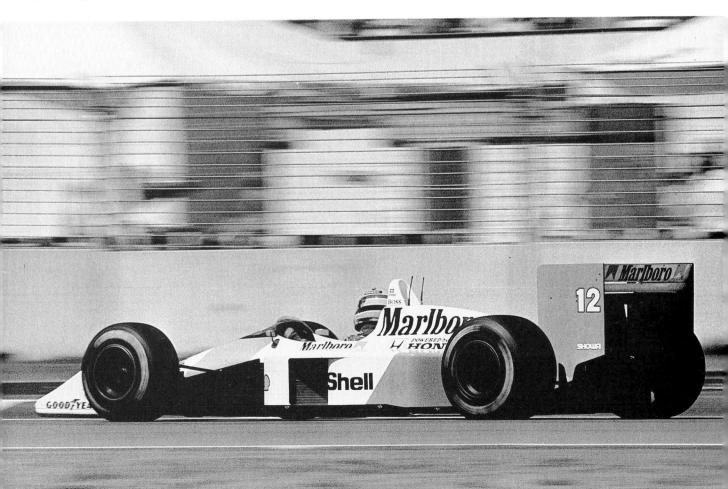

Diary

Imola (I) March 24

The MP4/4 first dusted its slicks in Italy, in a private session at Imola. Prost beat his fastest time from the recent Goodyear test at the circuit set in an interim RA-168-E-MP4/3 by no less than 1.5 seconds. Both Prost and Senna wound up with the astonishing time of 87.8 seconds.

Rio-Jacarepagua (BZ) April 3
Brazilian Grand Prix
Senna.... Q: 1/R:DQ
Prost ..... Q: 3/R:1

Rio de Janiero confirmed the message of the Imola test. Senna was quickest without undue trouble. However, it was a surprise to find Mansell's Judd-Williams splitting the two MP4/4s in an elite group of three sub-89 second runners. Driving as a man inspired, Mansell got to within six tenths of Senna's time while Gerhard Berger's Ferrari was just a hair's breadth away from joining the group. The rest of the field was nowhere, failing to crack one and a half minutes. Prost suffered monocoque delamination and he raced the spare car.

Senna's car suffered a broken gear linkage as he started the warm up lap so he started Prost's patched up car from the pit lane. That left Mansell alone on the front row but (though slower to get off the line) Prost was ahead before the first corner and the early laps showed him to be very much in charge. Though Berger further demoted Mansell on the first lap he was unable to pressure the leader. Meanwhile Piquet's Honda-Lotus held a distant fourth place and Senna was tearing through the pack. He had finished the first lap 21st but by the tenth lap he was eighth and the 18th

of 60 laps found him fourth.

Mansell had regained ground lost to Berger but now retired with ancillary failure. At the end of lap 20 Berger pitted for the first of two sets of fresh tyres and Senna swept into second place, half a minute adrift of Prost. With both MP4/4s running through on only one stop it looked all over bar the finishing order of the McLaren team. However, a flat battery delayed Senna's stop, then he was black flagged for switching cars after the green flag. That long awaited, ultimately inevitable decision left Prost to stroke home ahead of Berger while Piquet collected third only after the demise of Thierry Boutsen's Cosworth/Ford-Benetton.

Monza (I) April 21

Senna crashed heavily during the course of a three day Goodyear test at the Italian circuit, comprehensively damaging the chassis he was sharing with Prost. Nevertheless, Senna had the glory of the quickest lap (88.8 seconds). Piquet's Lotus evaluated a revised version of the RA-168-E engine, the XE2, which overcame a problem with the new pop off valve.

Imola (I) May 1
San Marino Grand Prix
Senna.... Q: 1/R:1
Prost.... Q: 2/R:2

Qualifying for the San Marino Grand Prix at Imola on May 1 reinforced the view that McLaren was in a class of its own. Piquet was third fastest, half a second away from breaking the elusive 90 second barrier. Senna took pole on 87.148s, Prost replied with 87.919s. Meanwhile Alessandro Nannini's Benetton outqualified Berger's Ferrari, getting to within a tenth of Piquet's time. But MI was so far ahead. This was the potential of which the MI drivers had spoken at Rio.

This time Senna was left out on his own as Prost's engine all but died at the start. Engulfed by the pack, Prost

completed the first lap in sixth place and he took eight laps to claw up to second place. He assumed station eight seconds behind Senna and that remained the situation all the way to the flag with the rest sliding a lap behind, in spite of Imola's heavy demands on fuel and the fact that Senna's car was occasionally jumping out of gear. Even Piquet finished a lap down. Worried about fuel consumption Piquet was attacked first by Nannini, then by Mansell, then by Boutsen. Boutsen was the only one of the quick atmo trio to finish, and he did so comfortably ahead of Berger if fractionally behind the Lotus.

Monte Carlo (MC) May 15
Monaco Grand Prix
Senna.... Q: 1/R:NR
Prost.... Q: 2/R:1

Through the streets of Monte Carlo the combination of the RA-168-E and the MP4/4 was just as effective as usual and Senna took pole position with a time over two and a half seconds quicker than Berger's third placed Ferrari. Once again Prost had to take second place to the team's new recruit while Michele Alboreto at last came into the frame, securing the second row for Ferrari. Mansell and Nannini broke into the top six to head the atmo challenge while Piquet failed to break into the top ten. Teammate Nakajima had failed to qualify, then a first corner incident took out the car proudly bearing number one...

Prost by then had already made a rare error, missing his shift into second gear. That left him snapping at Berger's heels as Senna drew steadily away. Try as he might Prost could not find a way past the Ferrari and Mansell came up to fill his mirrors - only for the Judd car to overheat. Over the first half of the race Senna pulled out an average of just about one second per lap. Eventually, just after two thirds distance Prost got his act to-

• Diary continues on page 78

gine. Ferrari couldn't match Honda V6 performance under race or qualifying conditions and the fuel efficiency of the Honda-McLaren package was such that only on rare occasions did the fuel free atmo cars get a look in on race day. Not until the penultimate event did a 3.5 litre machine assume the lead of a race.

Race fuel efficiency is heavily dependent upon the overall car package and the McLaren International side of the equation was equally impressive as that of its Japanese partner. Rivals had only seen the Brabham BT55's dismal track record - Murray had seen its original wind tunnel performance and knew the low line concept was a major breakthrough. The MP4/4 proved it to the world.

The MP4/4 was found to be particularly easy to balance, a hallmark of a sound design. Throughout the season relatively soft springs were run - typically 800lbs. at the front, 1000lbs. at the rear - while the downforce characteristics were flexible enough to accept reasonable changes in pitch. MI tried the car lower and far more stiffly sprung but the drivers hated it. The doubled

curvature diffuser ramp worked well with almost any ride height, the car running lower and harder without a major improvement in underwing performance. However, Murray admits that over the season the tendency was to go progressively stiffer. The '87 car couldn't have been stiffened up in such a manner since it had lacked torsional rigidity.

Nevertheless, the MP4/4 did not become a track hugging no droop suspension special. It did not need to. Its low line concept was a major step in overall aerodynamic efficiency and given its horsepower advantage, MI could afford to pull more wing than an atmo car. The likes of Williams, March and Benetton had to scratch harder for performance from the underwing and thus ran significantly lower and stiffer throughout the season. With its greater wheel movement the MP4/4 tended to be more controllable and it worked well just about anywhere, other than at Silverstone. Further, it was "amazingly easy to set up", according to race engineer Tim Wright: "it was easier to set up than the MP4/3 and it could be dialled in very

MP4/4 project leader Steve Nichols discusses the radical machine first time out at Imola with Prost (in car) and Senna. On this shakedown run the well sorted MP4/3 interim car's time was beaten by an amazing 1.5 seconds. By the time the new car reached Monte Carlo (overleaf) it had proved itself to be in a class of its own. Senna is pictured in the streets.

gether and overtook Berger. He had earlier got alongside on a number of occasions. This time he got a better exit from Rascasse and passed into Ste. Devote, immediately pulling away and eating into Senna's lead which had stabilised at around 50 seconds.

Senna replied with a series of faster laps and Dennis suggested both drivers to back off. They accepted, Senna's concentration lapsed and he met the barrier at Portier. Prost was handed the trophy while the Ferrari drivers filled the lower rungs of the rostrum, the only other runners on the same lap. Mansell, of course, had been ahead of Alboreto and he had tangled with the Ferrari as he fell back with his overheating problem. Nannini and Riccardo Patrese in the second Williams had never been far behind Alboreto but had likewise failed to last the distance due to frustrating 'traffic incidents'.

Woking (GB) May 18

Repairs at the factory kept MI away from the Goodyear test at Paul Ricard. Meanwhile, down in the south of France Piquet had the glory of fastest time. He tested another new version of the RA-168-E, this the XE3 destined for use in Mexico City.

Mexico City (MX) May 29
Mexican Grand Prix
Senna.... Q: 1/R:2
Prost.... Q: 2/R:1

Ferrari engine modifications saw Berger giving the McLaren men cause to look over their shoulders during qualifying. Prost had set up problems and only beat Berger by a whisker while Senna wound up just over half a second clear after a more comfortable two days. Piquet was best of the rest, a second and a half from pole. Next up were Alboreto and Nakajima, the second Lotus much higher placed than usual. Mexico City's thin high altitude air robbed the 'atmo' engines of charge pressure and no 3.5 litre car featured this weekend.

Sunday saw both Lotus' race engines fail, Piquet's while the World Champion was fending off Alboreto's Ferrari in the late stages. Piquet had held second initially, only to slip back behind Senna before the end of the first lap, then into the clutches of the Ferrari team. Over a lap ahead of his battle with Alboreto in the late stages, Berger was chasing hard with little hope of preventing a McLaren one - two.

Prost had taken the initiative at the start while Senna struggled with a prematurely opening pop off valve. The problem recurred on occasion but a greater worry for Senna was uncomfortably high fuel and tyre consumption. First he lost grip at the front, then at the rear. Nevertheless, he was able to run home out of Berger's grasp if no challenger for Prost, even though the leading car was forced to slow. For a long time Prost had been suffering high water temperature thanks to a helmet visor tear off obstructing a cooling air flow. His Honda engine proved characteristically strong.

Montreal (CDN) June 12
Canadian Grand Prix
Senna.... Q: 1/R:1
Prost.... Q: 2/R:2

The Circuit Gilles Villeneuve in Montreal was heavy on fuel, to the extent that Boutsen and Nannini were able to dispose of both of the faster qualifying Ferraris early on. However, flat out in a Benetton did not match economy race pace in a McLaren and as Nannini fell by the wayside Boutsen could but hope for a retirement ahead. Prost again suffered high water temperature to which was added brake troubles but this only served to consolidate Senna's advantage, not to elevate Boutsen.

Senna had qualified on pole, a whisker only ahead of Prost, a second clear of Berger, and had taken the advantage from his faster-starting teammate as they lapped back markers. In third place, Boutsen ran out the only other finisher on the same lap. Berger and Alboreto had long retired with electrical and engine failure respectively. Ferrari had made further engine modifications as witness the closing gap in qualifying but the early race evidence was of power won at the expense of fuel economy. Meanwhile, Lotus was once again overshadowed, Piquet finishing fourth and lapped for sheer lack of pace.

Detroit (USA) June 19
US Grand Prix
Senna.... Q: 1/R:1
Prost.... Q: 4/R:2

While Nannini had headed the atmo runners on the grid in Canada, one week later that honour went to Boutsen. This time around Berger closed to within a second of Senna and both Maranello cars outqualified Prost who was half a second up on Boutsen but almost one and a half seconds slower than Senna. Detroit was a circuit Prost hated.

Prost was again no threat to Senna (who was driving the T car) on race day, though the first six laps saw him rise magnificently from fifth to second place, setting what would stand as fastest lap on lap four. That rise was indicative of the continuing McLaren superiority, the rest now just about resigned to the role of also rans.

Prost might have thrown his dislike of the circuit aside for this race but he was subsequently hampered by a gearchange problem. Nevertheless, his second spot was never in doubt. In the race for third Boutsen and Berger collided early on, later Nannini and

• Diary continues on page 80

quickly to almost any circuit".

The exception to the rule, Silverstone, was the one circuit particularly well suited to a track hugging design since it was flat and very smooth and called for little in the way of harsh braking or acceleration to cause unsettling attitude changes. There was little to be gained from realistic wheel movement at Silverstone, much to lose. It was noticeable that the very low running, very stiffly sprung March ran well on this track in spite of its lack of horsepower (the latter evident in a 15m.p.h. or more top speed handicap).

Away from Silverstone, the ease of set up with the MP4/4 was particularly important for MI given that a 1988 Formula One car had to be fielded at 16 very different venues over the course of the season. This factor regularly helped put the team a step ahead of its opposition. Further, the balance of the car didn't alter greatly from full to empty tanks so it could be set up properly on half tanks. Again time was saved for other important matters during practice, while race performance naturally benefited.

Prost never did come to like the BT55 driving position and throughout the season he sat a little more upright than Murray intended, the top of his helmet then about half an inch higher than it should have been. Bob Bell later tested the effect of this in the wind tunnel and found a measurable difference. That fact emphasises the importance of the low line concept. The MP4/4 was a car of which Colin Chapman - racing's great innovator - could have been proud.

Sadly the conventional '88 Lotus chassis failed to live up to the Chapman heritage: in spite of an identical engine it was beaten from the moment it was fired up in Rio. Indeed, from the moment, a week earlier, when the prototype MP4/4 rolled out onto the Imola tarmac (so tauntingly close to Maranello).

The final major pre-season test had just been held at the Dino Ferrari circuit and had seen Prost head the timesheets in an interim MP4/3 chassied car, posting a time of 89.3 seconds compared to a Ferrari best of 89.9 seconds. The MP4/4 was meanwhile undergoing final assembly. The Honda deal had been late, the new package had been very thoroughly evaluated in the wind tunnel and the build programme had

• Diary continued

Alboreto did likewise. Those incidents cost the chances of all but Boutsen and he once more came through to make up the rostrum trio, this time a lap down. Meanwhile Lotus fortunes had fallen right back to the Monaco level, Nakajima failing to qualify and Piquet spinning out of midfield.

Paul Ricard (F) July 3
French Grand Prix
Senna.... Q: 2/R:2
Prost.... Q: 1/R:1

A new look to the grid: Prost on pole, half a second clear of Senna, threequarters of a second clear of Berger. Senna's final bid was thwarted by a mysteriously slow track but there was no denying Prost's form. To quote *Autocourse*: "Prost, once in the cockpit at Ricard, had grown horns. He took pole - his first in two years - and then carried the race to Senna, eclipsing him with an overtaking move which will go down as a classic of its kind.

"To be fair to Senna, he had struggled with a gearbox problem for most of the race and the chances are he could have beaten Prost. But we will never know. What was apparent, however, was Prost's bold assertion that he did not intend to be a push-over..."

Senna in fact suffered a worse repeat of his Imola gear selection problem. Prost had led from the start under pressure from Senna, a slower tyre stop costing him the lead and forcing his determined overtaking manoeuvre. Once ahead again, Senna's gear problem together with flat spotted tyres ensured the outcome.

In the wake of the now familiar McLaren demonstration, Ferrari had headed Benetton, had headed Lotus

on the grid, these six runners spanned by two seconds. Piquet got the jump on the Cosworth cars in front at the start and held fifth to the finish, a lap down. As was Berger, who couldn't match Alboreto's fuel economy. A lost second gear cost Piquet a chance of demoting the Austrian's thirsty Ferrari.

Silverstone (GB) July 10
British Grand Prix
Senna.... Q: 3/R:1
Prost.... Q: 4/R:NR

Silverstone gave Ferrari an unexpected edge in qualifying. Berger and Alboreto outran Senna and Prost, Berger clinching pole with a time half a second quicker than Senna's best effort. The circuit was well suited to the Ferrari engine characteristics and the team had more qualifying power for this race. Meanwhile MI could not find its usual chassis balance.

Finding the sort of chassis performance that McLaren sought in vain, the Judd-March paring of Mauricio Gugelmin and Ivan Capelli was next in line, albeit a second further adrift. To the delight of the atmo runners the race was wet. That was Prost's undoing.

'The Professor' had no experience of a carbon-carbon clutch in the wet and made a hash of the start. Swamped by the pack, he disappeared in the midfield spray. After two dozen uncertain tours grappling with somewhat erratic handling and already lapped, he called it a day. It was later discovered that his nose box had been incorrectly fitted. Meanwhile, Senna had taken charge after following Berger's rooster tail for 14 laps. Once ahead he drew steadily away, both Maranello machines registering poor fuel consumption, the penalty of increased engine power.

Indeed, the Ferraris fell pray to the fastest atmo runners. First to elbow by were Nannini and Mansell. A trip into the gravel dropped Nannini behind the Williams which had found a resurgence of form following the abandon-

ment of a computer controlled 'reactive' suspension system. Gugelmin, the sole surviving March driver, came through to fourth, ahead of Piquet while both Ferraris had run out of fuel...

Hockenheim (D) July 15

Senna registered quickest lap during a rain hit Goodyear test, lapping over two and a half seconds quicker than Boutsen, three and a half seconds quicker than Piquet with Ferrari studying times slower still. Rain upset form but there was no doubt about the continuing McLaren superiority.

Hockenheim (D) July 24
German Grand Prix
Senna.... Q: 1/R:1
Prost.... Q: 2/R:2

MI really was back on form: Senna a quarter of a second ahead of Prost, one and a half seconds ahead of Berger. Another one and a half seconds back was Piquet, fifth in the wake of Alboreto. On this fast circuit Senna was over three and a half seconds faster than Nannini's quickest atmo car, sixth on the grid.

The race started on a damp track, only Piquet risking slicks. He spun out on the first lap. Meanwhile Senna strode away as a slow-starting Prost chased Berger and Nannini. Prost was in the spare car having damaged his chassis on a kerb in qualifying. He took a dozen laps of the long and drying circuit to climb to second. Well in the groove, he then tried to catch Senna but was delayed lapping a couple of backmarkers. Working extremely hard in closing the gap to 12.5 seconds, he pushed a little too hard: a spin left him almost half a minute adrift, the finishing order settled. Berger claimed third, Alboreto fourth after Nannini suffered a throttle linkage problem. Capelli was the final finisher on the lead lap.

• Diary continues on page 82

Prost leads Senna at Paul Ricard. The Frenchman came alive at his home Grand Prix showing the determined Senna that he intended to win another World Championship in spite of his cautious approach to racing.

started too late to make Imola. However, MI had aimed to attend in view of its new relationship with Honda and in the event the prototype was flown out in a privately chartered cargo plane to run in a special day and a half session at the track.

Team Manager Jo Ramirez flew out with the prototype and witnessed an amazing new car debut. "In 27 years of racing I had never experienced anything like it. We didn't have to touch it at all - it kept going quicker and quicker. It ended up one and a half seconds faster than the old car. Without any development. Imola was incredibly encouraging".

Prost and Senna's MP4/4 shared time of 87.8 seconds literally straight out of the box was nothing short of sensational. A little cockpit

padding added here and there was all it took from the technical team. The news of the remarkable clocking sent shock waves through the Grand Prix world.

Just eleven days later the prototype was joined by two other freshly painted chassis at Rio, 03 dispatched on the last possible direct Varig flight, leaving Heathrow on the Wednesday evening prior to the race and arriving in the pit lane Thursday evening. Short on test time, on Saturday evening the MI drivers spoke of a lot of untapped potential within the new car while the Ferrari drivers admitted already to feeling overshadowed by Honda in the power stakes.

For his part, Mansell was realistic about his season long chances, in spite of his impressive qualifying effort. It was evident that the '88 Judd

Silverstone (GB) July 27

A major test at Silverstone brought out MI and the leading atmo cars, Prost recording the fastest lap. He was a whisker slower than Senna's third fastest qualifying time at the Grand Prix.

Hungaroring (H) August 7
Hungarian Grand Prix
Senna.... Q: 1/R:1
Prost.... Q: 7/R:2

The low grip Hungaroring gave the atmo runners renewed hope and in qualifying Mansell came within two tenths of a second of ousting Senna from pole. Boutsen, Capelli, Nannini and Patrese were next up, Prost languishing seventh with a lap just over a second off Senna's pace. At the end of the first lap Prost was even further down, in ninth place. However, he spent the remaining laps to two thirds distance rising slowly but surely through the order, all the time gaining on Senna. It was clear that he had the faster race set-up.

Meanwhile Senna had led from the start, but under pressure. First he had to shrug off Mansell - a high speed spin dropped the Williams after it got too close - next it was a case of keeping Patrese in check, with Boutsen and the chastised Mansell poised to profit from any setback. Patrese suffered a cracked exhaust and that gave Boutsen his turn to put the pressure on Senna, while Prost came through to demote both Williams representatives. Having in turn been passed by the flying Prost, Boutsen kept the leaders close company.

Senna was thus facing his fourth challenger, his most serious challenger. Although Prost was clearly

quicker than Senna he didn't manage to dislodge the Brazilian smartly, and when he did get by he was going too fast: Senna slotted back into the lead as Prost slid onto the rough.

Thereafter a wheel vibration - doubtless a legacy of the off course excursion - made Prost's task seem hopeless. Having seen daylight for just a few yards, he finished a mere half a second adrift while Boutsen suffered a cracked exhaust in the closing stages and consequently finished almost half a minute further back. Teammate Nannini was out of luck, while both Marches and both Williams found trouble though Gugelmin and Patrese finished fifth and sixth respectively. Berger had risen to claim fourth, the last finisher unlapped, his car no longer the handful it had been in qualifying.

Monza (I) August 19

Berger was the star of this Goodyear test, lapping almost a second faster than Senna. It was generally reckoned that Ferrari was running somewhat more than 2.5 bar in an effort to boost morale.

Spa Francorchamps (B) August 28
Belgian Grand Prix
Senna ..... Q: 1/R:1
Prost.... Q: 2/R:2

Berger was back pressurising the McLarens in the Ardennes, winding up within a second of pole in spite of a pop off valve problem. Senna it was who again got the verdict, and Alboreto rounded out the four runners within two seconds of his time. Fifth was Patrese - three and a half seconds adrift. Mansell was absent, suffering chickenpox. For a change, Nakajima was the fastest Lotus runner, almost four seconds from pole.

The race, such as it was, was over the first few laps. Prost got the jump on a wheelspinning Senna and led into La Source, then Senna retook the advantage under braking for Les Coombes.

Berger challenged Prost at the same spot on the second lap but a misfire soon had the Ferrari in the pits. Senna and Prost were then left alone, inferior car settings costing Prost any chance of making a fight of it. He was running less downforce and his chances worsened as the track got more slippery.

With Berger's demise Alboreto looked set for a distant third but ten laps from home his engine let go handing Boutsen another rostrum finish. Nannini and Capelli were next up, ahead of Piquet who was coping with brake problems. Senna's victory equalled the record seven Grand Prix victories in one season jointly to the credit of Prost and Jim Clark. Prost commented that he now felt his Championship chances "zero" even though he trailed by only three points - the total number of wins would determine the outcome and he was three adrift.

Monza (I) September 11
Italian Grand Prix
Senna.... Q: 1/R:10-NR
Prost.... Q: 2/R:NR

The race that Ferrari had to get right. Berger again came close in qualifying, but not close enough. Senna was the only driver to - just - break the 86 second barrier, taking a record tenth pole position in one season. Prost was three tenths slower, Berger another four tenths adrift. That was in spite of a spin on his best run which he reckoned cost his chance of splitting the MP4/4s. Predictably Alboreto consolidated the second row while Piquet was outqualified by the Megatron-Arrows, which were going better than ever and were the fastest cars in a straight line. Eighth quickest, Boutsen was the first of the atmo runners, almost three seconds slower than Senna.

The race for the lead lasted less than the length of the pits straight. Snatching third, Prost found his engine misfiring. Handed the advantage before the first chicane, Senna pulled a com-

• Diary continues on page 84

and Cosworth V8s could not match Honda or Ferrari 2.5 bar turbo-strength. The fastest atmo car was all but 10m.p.h. off Prost's highest straight-line speed of 184.92m.p.h. The Honda and Ferrari engines had yet to show their performance under 150 litre race conditions, of course. Sunday April 3 brought the acid test and a convincing pole for Senna was followed by a convincing victory for Prost.

Thus, lack of testing had not stopped MI getting the Ayrton and Alain Show underway on cue. Overall, 16 performances saw a total of 15 poles (13 to Senna) and 15 wins (eight to Senna) backed by 10 second places, a fourth and a sixth. All but five of the 32 starts were from the front row, and all but one were from the top two rows. MI literally hammered its opposition which might as well have given up at the mid way point. The first half of the season ended with Honda-McLaren having amassed 102 points while Ferrari was next in the Constructors' Cup chase with a mere 34.

In the closer Driver's title fight, Prost was understandably less inclined to take risks than the hungry Senna. Both drivers were immensely talented, Senna had the greater motivation. *Motoring News'* Grand Prix correspondent David Tremayne wrote that, "Quite simply Senna took more chances than anyone else, drove his car to his and its limits - both amazingly high - at all times and was the totally committed professional...

"In the Iberian races he didn't set his car up as well as Prost and paid the price, but it was in Portugal that he pulled the one really inexcusable stunt of the year by lunging so dangerously at Prost as they vied for the lead past the pits. It was a manoeuvre unworthy of such talent, and a forced indication of just how badly he wanted the crown...

"Overall, however, one can only nitpick if one seeks to criticise Senna as a race driver, because he lives and breathes racing, thinks like a winner and lets it all hang out. A lot of drivers just talk a good race. Senna grabs his by the throat. He is a doer. In 1988 he was the fastest, hungriest, most committed driver, and he won. And that was no more than his just desert".

Prost, of course, scored more points overall, in spite of his more cautious - but no less profes-

sional - approach. But 1988 was about winning, not about points gathering. The more mature Prost scored one win less than the whipper-snapper.

Of the five - and only five over the entire season - non-scoring McLaren drives, one had ended in a voluntary withdrawal prompted by a combination of a poor (clutch troubled) start, difficult handling and atrocious conditions. This was Prost at Silverstone, making a widely condemned move. But by mid season it was clear that only wins would count when it came to determining the destiny of the Driver's crown: the fact that there was little to be gained from mere points gathering helped prompt Prost's withdrawal from mid field, a lap behind Senna and falling back. His difficult car was later found to have an incorrectly fitted nose box.

Twice Senna shunted a perfectly good car out of a race - at Monte Carlo and at Monza - while at Rio he was disqualified for switching to the spare after the green flag, his race car suffering a disconnected gear linkage. A bush failed when the lever was pushed forward to select first gear. It was later found that the part had been machined too much. It was a one off fault: probably the production rush had allowed the rogue bush to slip out without passing through the inspection department.

The only mechanical failure to put a car in the dead car park after the green light was Prost's engine failure at Monza. At the preceding Francorchamps race Nakajima's Honda had failed due to a piston collapse. At Monza Prost's engine lapsed onto five cylinders then he too suffered a piston collapse. Honda later discovered the cause of these uncharacteristic engine failures but for political reasons it prefers to shoulder the blame rather than comment further.

In the light of Prost's problem Senna was advised to richen his mixture. He was already running into deficit on fuel having raced Prost hard in the early stages and towards the end of the race he was having to nurse his car home. With Berger closing he looked to be under tremendous pressure, which would help explain the collision with Schlesser. However, Ramirez says that the team did not feel that the Ferrari was getting dangerously close: "Senna could have waited.

• Diary continued

fortable cushion then eased off to Prost's slightly compromised pace. Yet at half distance Prost pushed harder, set fastest lap and over a series of three laps he halved the gap to Senna - in spite of the misfire. Senna had only just begun to respond when Prost lost speed and steadily fell back into the clutches of Berger's distant Ferrari. From third place, with 15 of 51 laps to run Prost headed for the pits, there to remain. It was an engine malady: piston failure was suspected. Much earlier, Nakajima had suffered engine failure (while Piquet had spun out blaming clutch trouble).

Senna was instructed to run his engine richer and to handle it with the utmost care. He did just that, his caution lopping two or three seconds off his pace. In response Berger speeded up. The gap fell from two dozen to less than ten seconds with five laps to run. At that stage Senna increased his speed but Berger kept coming and he was drawing Alboreto with him. Did Senna's rich running car have the fuel left to fend off the red cars, cars urged on by every voice in Italy? The question remains unanswered since on the penultimate lap, the Ferraris now clearly visible in his mirrors, Senna tangled with a backmarker. Mansell stand-in Jean Louis Schlesser saw Senna coming as he braked for the chicane and he tried to keep out of the way, only to get on the loose. Impatient, Senna forged through the chicane while Schlesser fought his wayward machine. The Gods were in charge of Schlesser's path. Not long departed this world, Ferrari must have smiled down as the two cars collided.

So it was that the combination of McLaren and Honda lost a race, for the first time in 12 events. Berger swept home triumphantly ahead of Alboreto while the Arrows drivers were next up - Eddie Cheever taking the rostrum - and Capelli won the atmo race after both Benettons ran into trouble. Senna was classified tenth (and thankfully the delighted Tifosi didn't lynch the MI party sent out to retrive his broken car).

Estoril (P) September 25
Portugese Grand Prix
Senna.... Q: 2/R:6
Prost.... Q: 1/R:1

Estoril offered the atmo runners a better chance, as witness Capelli's third quickest qualifying time, ousting Berger from his regular spot. Capelli was a second slower than Senna while, surprisingly, Senna was in turn half a second slower than Prost.

There were two starts (three, including an aborted attempt) thanks to a midfield incident and Senna ousted Prost each time. However, at the end of the first lap of the restarted race Prost got a better run onto the start/finish straight and drew out of Senna's slipstream, looking for the inside. Senna all but pushed him into the pits wall but Prost was not one to be intimidated. He left Senna the choice of conceding room or interlocking wheels. Prost, seething, was through.

Thereafter, Prost could breathe easy. Senna faced bad news on the fuel read out and had to resign himself to defending second place. Indeed, Capelli soon became the focus of his attention. Quarter distance found Prost comfortably ahead as Senna fended off Capelli's clearly quicker Judd-March. A few laps later the atmo car was through and off after Prost. Senna then came under attack from Berger. Berger similarly had the measure of Senna and he was able to close on Capelli as Capelli in turn narrowed the gap to Prost. Half distance found the top trio close, this race uncharacteristically open.

Then Berger went for the wrong switch and triggered his cockpit extinguisher, soon spinning out as a result of his right foot slipping off the soaked brake pedal. Meanwhile, Capelli was facing high water temperature readings. So it was that the heat went out of Prost's position. Senna was still under pressure, though, this time from Mansell. Mansell sustained his challenge right through the threequarter distance mark then hit the back of the McLaren as Senna avoided a backmarker who was rejoining after an off. Mansell was out, Senna was left with bent rear suspension and he finished sixth after a stop. Boutsen shared the rostrum with Prost and Capelli.

Jerez (E) October 2
Spanish Grand Prix
Senna.... Q: 1/R:4
Prost.... Q: 2/R:1

Jarama was another tight track, another chance for the atmos to shine. This time Mansell led the challenge, qualifying a mere two tenths from Senna's pole. Prost kept Mansell from the front row while Boutsen was the last runner under 85 seconds. Nannini, Capelli and Patrese kept Piquet, Berger and Alboreto to the bottom of the top ten, the Ferrari looking as unsuited at this circuit as it had at the Hungaroring.

Senna made a poor start from pole, slotting in behind Mansell while Prost took a firm grip on the proceedings. Senna made one over-ambitious stab at Mansell then had to settle for third, again facing a gloomy fuel picture. Thus it was Mansell rather than Senna who ensured that Prost could not relax. At least until the tyre stops: at that stage a sticking wheel nut took the wind out of Mansell's sails. Prost had a perfect stop and, without Senna's concern over fuel consumption, a rewarding race.

Meanwhile Senna had managed to shrug off Patrese but not Capelli, who overtook the Williams at half distance.

• Diary continues on page 86

Even if he had lost a second passing Schlesser, Berger would not have beaten him. In my view it was impatience. The same motivation that makes Senna win races, sometimes makes him lose them".

Earlier, at Monte Carlo, lack of pressure led to lack of concentration and misjudgement. At Adelaide Senna lost second gear and went well into deficit on fuel staving off Piquet. Senna used the lowest charge temperature and the richest mixture setting on the fast parts of the circuit then backed off for the slower section, where second gear was frequently required. Directed by Dennis, this tactic hid the problem from Piquet who did not press home his challenge. Senna was able to stroke into a comfortable second place.

This season, during the race the drivers primarily juggled with the charge air temperature control to trade economy for power, whereas previously the boost control switch had been the main tactical weapon. On 150 litres fuel was always tight, with Imola, Montreal, Silverstone and Hockenheim the most difficult circuits, Monaco and Detroit the easiest. At Monaco and Detroit the cars started with 140 litres on board, to help save weight, brakes and tyres. From Honda's point of view, Montreal turned out to be the greatest challenge according to project leader Goto.

Favouring atmo-instant throttle response, Estoril and Jerez were tough and at Jerez fuel became so tight that the race should by rights have fallen to an atmo car. Mansell finished less than 30 seconds behind victor Prost after suffering a sticking wheel nut. Eeking out his fuel, Prost drove a truly inspired race to keep the Judd-Williams at bay.

At Estoril both cars had suffered miscalibrated fuel read outs and consequently finished with a little surplus fuel on board (a problem not confined to this occasion). Senna also had high speed oversteer to cope with and managed no better than sixth, bugged by excessive consumption. At Jerez he was fourth, again complaining of poor handling and poor consumption. The

The McLaren MP4/4's central fuselage was kept down to the transverse dimensions of the compact Honda RA-168-E engine. The pop off is at the front of the plenum, reaching over the main fuel tank top located EMS black box.

• Diary continued

Capelli quickly dealt with Senna but it was too late to bid for the lead, and in any case his engine let go. Senna didn't bag third, though, Nannini coming through strongly to take the final rostrum position. Only three points for Senna, then, another nine for Prost. The Iberian excursion had put the French driver ahead on points. Nevertheless, he was starting to drop scores and victory in Japan would seal the crown for Senna.

Suzuka (J) October 30
Japanese Grand Prix
Senna.... Q: 1/R:1
Prost.... Q: 2/R:2

Few fuel consumption worries at the Honda-owned Suzuka race track, scene of countless test miles. Nor was there any serious doubt about McLaren annexing pole. Senna it was again, three tenths ahead of Prost. Berger was just over a second slower and Capelli joined him on the second row. Lotus fortunes improved with Piquet and Nakajima sharing the third row. Alas, the home hero made a hash of the getaway, finishing the first lap in twentieth place. Driving the T car, Senna was in trouble, too. He had stalled and he finished the lap eighth. Meanwhile, Prost convincingly led Berger and Capelli.

Senna took only four laps to reach fourth place. Two laps later Capelli passed Berger and went after Prost, setting a series of fastest laps. As Senna passed Berger on lap 11 Capelli had the lead McLaren in striking distance. Prost's gear change was playing up and leaving the final corner on the 16th lap, with Capelli on his tail he missed a ratio. Capelli drew alongside to lead for a few hundred yards across the start/finish line. Alas, three laps

later, with Senna closing in on the fight, the Judd car's engine died.

Senna was now perfectly placed, backmarkers starting to present a major challenge. As usual, his superior performance in traffic was a major suit, while Prost was still grappling with his gear selection problem, his clutch refusing to release properly. Rain spells assisted Senna's progress - he used the wettest portion of the race to latch onto Prost's tail.

At one stage Prost missed a gear and Senna all but hit him. This gear selection bother was the deciding factor: subsequently Senna sliced decisively through. Behind the Honda-McLaren one-two, Berger ran into fuel worries and was thus forced to give way to both Benettons, but he was able to repass Nannini with some assistance from Alboreto, who was a lap down having been out of the picture all weekend. For the crowd Nakajima's eventual seventh place was far more cheering. Piquet had retired.

Adelaide (AUS) November 13
Australian Grand Prix
Senna.... Q: 1/R:2
Prost.... Q: 2/R:1

Senna, of course, came to Adelaide as World Champion and it found him in cracking form. So was Prost - less than two tenths slower in qualifying. Mansell was next up, one and a half seconds down on Senna but a whisker ahead of Berger who in turn was a whisker ahead of Piquet. Prost again made a better start than Senna while Mansell was elbowed out by Berger and Piquet, the Lotus running untypically high. Berger also put in an uncharteristic performance, passing Senna on lap three, Prost on lap 14.

Berger had decided to run flat out regardless of the fuel situation for the sheer glory of leading the final race of the turbo era. How far he could have gone will never be known since just before one third distance he tripped up over a backmarker, retiring on the spot. That left Prost in command

while Senna found himself without second gear, a ratio used five times a lap. Meanwhile Piquet occupied himself with an attack from Patrese and Mansell.

Could Senna keep ahead of Piquet and the Williams duo? MI advised him to run a low charge temperature and a rich mixture on the fastest part of the circuit, easing back on fuel where second gear hampered his effort. That kept his lap times fast, concealing his problem from his pursuers. Senna's fuel consumption situation swung well into the red but the tactic worked: Piquet did not sense his chance and Senna was able to ease off enough at the end to bring his fuel situation back under control without loss of second spot.

Fine race management, then, brought MI another one - two while Piquet achieved his third rostrum finish of a disappointing season. Not once had he stood higher than the third rung. And Nakajima retired, once again failing to add to the single point he had scored in Rio. MI scored nine and a half times as many points as Lotus in the Constructors' Cup, three times as many as runner up Ferrari, four times as many as third placed Benetton.

fact that Senna lost out significantly more on fuel consumption than Prost on the two Iberian tracks was subsequently analysed by Honda using the real-time engine data recorded during the races.

It was found that Prost gained on fuel efficiency by continually up-shifting in a lower speed band than Senna. Prost drove more smoothly, using higher gears, his technique avoiding the less efficient high r.p.m. range, according to Honda's report. Instead he enjoyed marginally higher boost, the higher boost more efficiently exploiting power (aiding economy through improved cylinder charging).

Power is a function of torque and engine speed and given an atmospheric engine Senna's technique should have made better use of the available performance. Certainly in qualifying this year his throttle blipping turbocar technique was as effective as ever in keeping the turbos well spooled up. But his aggressive driving was not appropriate given the overriding importance of fuel efficiency on the Iberian circuits and, according to Honda: "after studying our analysis, Senna adapted his driving style to overcome the potential fuel efficiency problem at the Japanese Grand Prix".

Aside from the Iberian races, all finishes for the McLaren duo were in first and second places. That in spite of Senna's problem at Adelaide and the other transmission troubles at Imola, Detroit, Ricard and Suzuka. If the MP4/4 had an Achilles Heel, it was its gear change mechanism. More progress might have been made had MI not been busy developing a brand new transverse gearbox for 1989. As we have seen, lack of time had forced Murray to retain a conventional gear selection system, one carried over from the MP4/3 and which he considered "fundamentally archaic".

The new gearbox caused displeasure on a number of occasions, the change sluggish early on. Worse, at Imola and Ricard Senna found gears hard to select. At Ricard the upshot was constant over-revving but with its 14,000r.p.m. potential the RA-168-E could take that in its stride. Towards the end of the year MI tidied up the shift mechanism within the 'box and this brought improvement. Another modification was a larger bearing at the back of the lower gear shaft from Monza since the original bearing had

been proving rather short lived. Nevertheless, it had not failed during a race.

Of course, at Adelaide Senna suffered a stripped second gear and it was later found that a batch of faulty gears had slipped through the net. Aside from the gear selection problem, the three shaft gearbox proved reliable and it held its oil pressure properly, unlike the model it replaced. The oil pressure was always checked on Friday, the amount of oil adjusted to ensure always the minimum possible was run.

Prost's problem at Suzuka was a clutch release failure. The drivers were not very comfortable with the carbon-carbon clutch, particularly at the start of a race. The problem was acute in the wet - as witness Prost at Silverstone. The carbon-carbon clutch was run everywhere in testing and practice but not always was it raced.

At Rio Senna took the start in chassis 03, which had been intended as Prost's race car but had been found to lack structural rigidity: the front portion of the tub delaminated due to a manufacturing fault. This occurred after Prost had set fourth fastest time in the first qualifying session and the car was patched up to act as a muletta. Having been forced to race it, Senna drove it again in testing at Monza, prior to Imola. Half a dozen laps from the end of a long distance run his times suddenly dropped. With the benefit of a low fuel load he clearly wanted the glory of fastest lap. He got it but the tyres were not up to his pace and he paid for it, going off in a big way at the second Lesmo corner.

Senna escaped greatly shaken unhurt while the car was all but written off, a radiator thrust into the monocoque. Chassis 04 had to be pressed into service to replace it. One spare was run as a matter of policy. The fourth chassis required for Imola featured a stronger front end (to ensure no repeat of the Rio problem) and a slightly revised cockpit surround.

Through the first half of the season a number of car damaging incidents kept the pressure on the factory. Senna shunted again racing at Monaco - this tub (01) escaped but there was plenty of component damage - and both cars came back from the Ricard race with damaged monocoques. Prost hit a kerb early on and one of the skid plates buried itself in the tub floor while Senna punched a sizeable hole in his tub floor right

Pushing on at Ricard: overleaf. Here the Honda-McLarens exceeded 190m.p.h. but were not quite as fast as the Ferraris. Both Berger and Alboreto made 197m.p.h. passes, Prost a best of 191, Senna of 190m.p.h.

under his knees, probably again through contact with a kerb.

Kerb damage was not uncommon, monocoques regularly repaired for this reason, though Senna's cavity was exceptional. The tub in question (02) had been the spare car prior to Ricard and was out of service until Hungary where it resumed its life as T car. That followed the retirement of chassis 04 from the race team, following Prost's qualifying damage at Hockenheim: this time kerb contact had caused a cracked engine mount and a cracked floor.

For Silverstone 02 had been replaced by 05 while 06 was new for Estoril. Notably, Senna's collision with Schlesser did not cause tub damage, though the rear suspension of 05 was badly bent. Total production was six chassis, none of which were scrapped, two ending the season with test teams, one (03) as a show car.

Only two RA-168-E - MP4/3 interim cars had been built, the first running at Silverstone in December 1987, driven by Prost. It then ran at Estoril in the Goodyear test that month, and at Silverstone again prior to dispatch to Japan where Senna had his first run as a McLaren driver at Suzuka on February 16. Meanwhile the second interim car had appeared at Jerez, where Prost was fastest in the February Goodyear test in spite of problems with the new FISA-supplied pop off valve.

At Rio in the second week of March for another Goodyear test Prost was only fourth fastest in the same car, mainly due to engine related problems. In particular the new pop off valve was still a headache. After Rio came the March Imola test that preceded the MP4/4's debut. The pop off problem had still not been fully resolved. Not until the Imola race was it completely overcome, with the introduction of the XE2 version of the RA-168-E.

Not surprisingly, with the new car working well from the word go there was little alteration to the original chassis specification. The only significant chassis modification (other than the usual aerodynamic tuning) was revised front geometry introduced at the Monza test prior to Francorchamps. The aim was to switch from pro to anti-Akermann to help promote better turn in. Since this altered the turning arc of the front wheels extra steering lock was a spin-off benefit.

The steering arms picked up on new brackets slightly lower down on the upright and those pick up points were beefed up after Monza to ensure sufficient strength to resist kerb knocks on qualifying laps.

The low line, fuel efficient MP4/4 was one of the few '88 cars running without a two or even three tier rear wing package. An ultra-high downforce double decker wing was tried at Monaco, a triple decker version at Detroit, but only in qualifying. Rear wing dimensions were predictably altered in the summer for the high speed (plus 220k.p.h.) Silverstone, Hockenheim, Francorchamps and Monza circuits while a special low drag two rather than three element wing was tried inconclusively at Monza.

A two piece adjustable front wing skirt was toyed with towards the end of the season, from Estoril. The idea was to allow the skirt base to be kept precisely level with the monocoque floor. At Suzuka Prost ran the adjustable skirt only to suffer an aerodynamic imbalance which led to it being rejected for the second day of qualifying, so sensitive is aerodynamic set up. However, the adjustable system subsequently became standard wear.

The rear anti roll bar was rarely removed - it was soft and MI was not desperate for the small traction advantage to be gained from running without it. The cockpit damper control was rarely used and was thus established as not to be worth its weight and complexity.

Brake ducts naturally varied in size according to circuit demands. The aim was to run the smallest possible duct for minimum drag. Monte Carlo, Montreal, Detroit and Adelaide (a circuit notoriously harsh in its braking demands) were notable for large ducts. Sometimes ducts were taken off for qualifying runs. At Rio it was possible to run without brake cooling air, though the wheel bearings still needed cooling.

The periscope-type compressor intakes (emerging through the pod lids) survived only the first half of the season. Periscopes had been common in the days before pop off valves, adding a little pressure at the compressor inlet at the penalty of increased aerodynamic drag. Honda preferred the periscopes. Although running periscopes couldn't add to the ultimate pressure felt in the plenum chamber thanks to the pop off valve, a higher compressor inlet pressure was beneficial. It essence, it meant that the turbocharger didn't have to work as hard. It ran at reduced speed, improving response, with reduced back pressure improving power.

However, these gains were marginal and in the face of the faster circuits visited over the second half of the season it was decided that the aerodynamics of the chassis were a more important consideration. At the fast Silverstone circuit modified internal ducts were tried on the first day of qualifying. The aftercooler was shortened slightly leaving room for a vertical slot at its outside edge from which air was ducted to the compressor.

Untested, the new internal ducting was quickly removed in view of the aerodynamic imbalance experienced at the circuit. However, the new ducting wasn't the culprit and it duly returned for use throughout the second half of the season, enlarged as from Monza.

Of the three available turbo sizes, the smallest was never raced. The largest model was the regular equipment, both smaller units causing an uncomfortably steep inrush of power. The improved response of the medium sized turbo saw it replace the regular unit at street circuits but even so Prost ran the larger turbo at Adelaide for a more civilised power delivery. In terms of the turbo lag, there was no real difference. There was just a little lag this season: very slight yet significant in the face of the instant response of the atmo engines.

As we have noted, an even more significant factor at first was the adverse effect of the '88 specification pop off valve. This was of a completely different design to that run in '87 and was introduced late: Honda had only a month's warning of it's unfriendly characteristics, too little time in which to effect fundamental engine modification prior to Rio. The new pop off opened in a different manner and once opened pressure tumbled to 2.0 bar and still the valve didn't close properly.

Clearly, one could not afford to blow the pop off open. However, in the case of the XE1, on overrun the effect of a shut throttle and a still spinning compressor (the turbine not instantly stopping, of course) could cause pressure in the plenum to overshoot 2.5 bar. In blowing the pop

Over the second half of the season the periscope type compressor air intake as seen right was replaced by internal ducting, as seen below. This left a closed pod lid, as evident left, improving the car's aerodynamics.

off open, that adversely affected the next acceleration. The answer to the problem was in the form of the so called XE2, which was first run by Piquet at the Monza test prior to Imola and was run by all four Honda cars in the San Marino Grand Prix.

The XE2 changed the throttle position, removing the separate butterfly for each inlet tract and instead putting a butterfly in each bank's charge plumbing just ahead of the plenum inlet and thus ahead of the pop off. As a consequence, pressure build up behind the throttle on the overrun was not felt by the new FISA valve. While the six butterfly option had been identified as ideal, a further benefit of the new two butterfly system was of less turbulence in the inlet tract at part throttle. The higher turbulence had adversely affected carburation and reducing it assisted the quest to stabilise combustion.

Aside from the relocated butterflies, the only changes from XE1 specification were detail modifications to rings, oil seals and suchlike, primarily aimed at reducing friction. The XE2 was raced throughout the remainder of the season, except at Mexico City for which a special XE3 version was developed.

Due to the high altitude the Mexican air is thin - the pressure loss is around a quarter bar - so the turbine has to work harder. Back pressure becomes a potential problem, affecting volumetric efficiency and hence torque. Power is a function of torque and engine speed: Honda sought higher revs to compensate. Thus the XE3 employed an 82mm. bore size and it was apparently tuned for a higher peak power speed. It was a complete success and on occasion was tried for qualifying elsewhere thereafter (in particular, at Monza).

In Mexico the Lotus team experienced a fuel related problem that remained a mystery. That and the Francorchamps/Monza engine failures were the only trouble experienced by Honda once it had sorted its pop off problem.

In contrast, Ferrari struggled throughout the season as it strove unsuccessfully to match Honda-McLaren performance. By the end of 1987 Maranello's new iron block V6 engine had just about reached a competitive 4.0 bar power level but under the '88 conditions Ferrari found itself a step behind once more in spite of using an adaptation of the same unit. For '87 Ferrari had

switched from the familiar 120 degree aluminium alloy V6 of the early to mid Eighties to a 90 degree configuration linerless block exploiting a new cast iron alloy with interesting properties. Careful design had actually saved weight while strength was gained but loss of the excellent heat rejection of aluminium was the penalty.

The new generation Ferrari V6 was equipped with aluminium alloy four valve, single plug heads featuring a 32 degree included valve angle, matching that of the RA-168-E. Bore and stroke dimensions were 81.0×48.4mm, a stroke: bore ratio of 0.598. The valves were operated via bucket tappets, the mechanicals on the whole conventional and including Mahle oil gallery pistons and sodium cooled valves. Like Honda, Ferrari ran a full engine management system operating solenoid injectors, distributorless ignition and the wastegate. Significantly, the injection system worked at a pressure in the region of 10 bar whereas Bosch low pressure injection ran at 5 bar, the Honda system at an undisclosed level. Toluene fuel was naturally employed but the percentage of toluene appears to have been lower than the 84% figure quoted by Honda.

Further, Ferrari did not employ fuel heating. Apparently atomisation was a greater headache for Ferrari under 2.5 bar than for Honda. Atomisation was a key to fuel efficient performance.

The more successful 4.0 bar version of the Ferrari engine had started out in 1987 producing a quoted 880b.h.p. (which looked somewhat optimistic) at 11,500r.p.m. on an 8.0:1 compression ratio. Improvement, particularly in terms of combustion chamber detailing and inlet tract modification had seen the power level rise to a convincing 950b.h.p. in qualifying, 900b.h.p. in race trim by mid season. At this stage Ferrari is believed to have achieved levels of 4.1/4.2 bar through careful location of the pop off, a technique Honda is alleged to have pioneered.

The fact that pressure drops where air flow accelerates - as through a venturi - is the basis of carburettor operation and ground effect aerodynamics yet it did not occur to the FISA to control the exact positioning of its pop off valve within a given inlet system. Clearly, positioning the valve over a section of charge plumbing which constituted a venturi throat could pay dividends.

The Honda-Lotus, right, featured a more complex front wing assembly than that run of the MP4/4 and push rod front suspension. Meanwhile, the '88 Ferrari, below, was an updated '87 car retaining the same monocoque.

Position the pop off over a venturi and the mandatory maximum pressure will be felt at an artificially high charge flow rate. Either side of the venturi the flow is correct, the pressure is higher...

No self respecting engineer could miss an opportunity like that. However, Honda later denied positioning its valve over a venturi, saying that such a ploy was against the spirit of the regulations and was thus against Honda philosophy.

During the second half of the '87 season Garrett had supplied Ferrari with improved turbochargers featuring a silicon Nitride ceramic coating for the rotors, reducing rotor mass, and low friction bearings. Thus equipped Berger had taken pole on three occasions and memorable victories in Japan and Australia. However, at Rio in '88 it was immediately evident that he did not have equipment capable sustaining that level of success.

In the face of the '88 regulations Ferrari had increased its maximum engine speed to 12,000r.p.m. at which it quoted 620b.h.p. Among other revisions to the heads, the combustion chamber detailing had been modified together with an increase in compression ratio to 10.0:1. Like Honda, Ferrari immediately had a problem with the new pop off and in response it rigged up a system whereby the driver could press a button at the instant of pressure drop to quickly regain optimum performance via manipulation of the wastegate. This was followed by engine management system reprogramming to achieve the same effect automatically but not until a quarter of the season had run did Ferrari follow Honda's example and rejig its throttle system. It replaced its original six throttles with a single butterfly just ahead of the pop off at the front of the plenum.

By this stage - the Canadian Grand Prix - the maximum engine speed had increased to 12,600r.p.m. and power in the order of 650b.h.p. was available for qualifying. Race power was then in the region of 590-615b.h.p. according to the demands of the circuit. Subsequent development saw the injection pressure exceed 10 bar but not until Hungary did Ferrari introduced an aftercooler by-pass to control charge temperature, Honda-style. Even then it was still felt that

Honda enjoyed superior atomisation. Ferrari took its somewhat lucky Monza victory using a lower revving, higher torque engine that was more frugal. Ferrari could have power or economy, not both, as it showed at Silverstone. It never got on top of the challenge of 150 litre race power. Sometimes it was its own worst enemy - for example Berger supposedly lacked the fuel to challenge Senna in Mexico, only for the team to find a surplus of fuel in the tank at the end of the race.

Nor could Ferrari find an answer to Honda's 685b.h.p. qualifying specification allied to the low line MP4/4. After the trip to North America Ferrari put in some strong top speeds on fast circuits. However, only at Silverstone did it manage to oust MI from its customary position at the head of the timesheets. That feat suggests that the fast sweeps of the Northamptonshire circuit mysteriously favoured the conventional aerodynamics of the Barnard-developed Ferrari to those of the radical lowline MP4/4, which worked so impressively elsewhere. Barnard, though, likewise shunned a track hugging, no droop suspension chassis philosophy.

Certainly Ferrari had found more power for the second half of the season, albeit at the expense of fuel consumption while Silverstone was well suited to its engine characteristics, its narrow power band not the usual handicap. For its part, MI was suffering an uncharactistic aerodynamic imbalance.

The Ferrari F1/87/88 was an '87 chassis updated within the dictates of the clause that allowed retention of a feet ahead of the front wheel axis design in '88. Thus, the chassis structure remained unchanged while the aerodynamic package was revised, logically taking advantage of the smaller aftercoolers. Nevertheless, the car remained starkly traditional alongside Murray's low line machine. Interestingly, late in the season Ferrari toyed with a cockpit-adjustable front ride height control.

The Ferrari F1/87 had been created by Harvey Postlethwaite and Gustav Brunner with final design approval by Barnard upon his arrival at Maranello in late '86, fresh from MI. There is no doubt that as a conventional late Eighties design it was one of the very best and the opening of Ferrari's own rolling road wind tunnel had helped

In his Formula Thr days Piquet sometim unbuckled his belts ar slid down in his seat improve airflow. 1988 he had to s upright (above) whi Prost (top photograp

94

...d Senna were far ...ore reclined. The ...mparative heights of ...e cockpit coaming ...ustrate the difference ...tween a conventional ...te Eighties car and a ...w liner.

Barnard hone its performance to match the performance of any '87 rival. In '88 it was overshadowed by the performance of the MP4/4 everywhere except Silverstone, on circuits putting a premium on power and equally on those putting a premium on grip. In turn the F1/87/88 overshadowed the performance of the Honda-Lotus with monotonous regularity.

The Lotus 100T was the only brand new 1988 turbocar aside from the MP4/4. However, not only was it old fashioned aerodynamically compared to the low line MP4/4, it had another inherent disadvantage in its angled powertrain. As well as wasting the potential of the low V6

CHASSIS LOG

1

New for Senna at Rio (not raced). For Senna at Imola, Monte Carlo, Mexico City, Montreal and Detroit (not raced). T car at Paul Ricard, Silverstone and Hockenheim (raced by Prost). For Prost at Hungaroring, Spa Francorchamps and Monza. Subsequently became Japanese test car.

2

New as T car at Rio (raced by Prost). T car at Imola, Monte Carlo, Mexico City, Montreal and Detroit (raced by Senna). For Senna at Paul Ricard. T car at Hungaroring, Spa Francorchamps, Monza, Estoril, Jerez and Suzuka (raced by Senna). For Senna at Adelaide.

3

New for Prost at Rio (raced by Senna). Damaged Monza test, subsequently became European test car.

4

New for Prost at Imola. For Prost at Monte Carlo, Mexico City, Montreal, Detroit, Paul Ricard, Silvestone and Hockenheim (not raced). Damaged qualifying at Hockenheim, subsequently became show car.

5

New for Senna at Silverstone. For Senna at Hockenheim, Hungaroring, Spa Francorchamps, Monza, Estoril, Jerez and Suzuka (not raced). T car at Adelaide.

6

New for Prost at Estoril. For Prost at Jerez, Suzuka and Adelaide.

that lifted the centre of gravity of the engine and transaxle a small but significant amount. TWR had built a Le Mans special version of its Group C XJR-8 with a similarly angled powertrain and had found that it destroyed handling. Although the Group C car's powertrain was much heavier, there has to be some parallel there. The 100T certainly suffered a lack of mechanical grip which was tackled via unsuccessful suspension modifications.

Early on, at the first Monza test Lotus found an apparent fuel consumption advantage compared to MI. The following weekend's Imola walkover consequently came as a real shock. No doubt about it, the Honda-Lotus was a poor package. The failure of Lotus to match MI given an identical engine and the services of the reigning World Champion underlined the excellence of the MP4/4.

Of the under-powered atmo cars, the Judd-March had arguably the most effective chassis, though the Benetton was also impressive. The Williams suffered inadequate cooling for the first half of the season - its Judd engine tended to overheat and lose power after only 10 laps - while its 'reactive' suspension sapped power and simply didn't work as intended. March designer Adrian Newey had devised an unconventional aerodynamic package around a tall engine, as had Benetton designer Rory Byrne, both packages based on the philosophy of track hugging. The March was superbly well balanced and had the glory of leading a race while the Cosworth/Ford-Benetton proved a useful points gatherer for Boutsen.

Those conventional atmo engines, the Judd CV and the Cosworth DFR could not muster more than 600b.h.p., running to only 11,000r.p.m. Back in 1983 the 3.0 litre DFY had produced 520b.h.p. running to a similar peak power speed, which represents the same 173.3b.h.p. per litre, or 15.75b.h.p. per litre per 1000r.p.m. That figure per 1000r.p.m. was a representative figure for an Eighties four valve atmospheric race engine running on 102 octane fuel, which limited it to a 12.5:1 compression ratio. A Formula 3000 engine restricted to 9,000r.p.m. was capable of producing over 16b.h.p. per litre per 1000r.p.m. thanks to the superior breathing and burning possible at the enforced lower speed.

In the summer of 1988 MI unveiled a Honda V10 test car based on the MP4/4 monocoque and this went to Jerez in the autumn where it lapped almost two seconds faster than the turbocar had managed at the Spanish Grand Prix meeting. Of course, Jerez is a circuit well suited to the instant response of an atmospheric car. Nevertheless, the Jerez performance suggested that the prototype V10 must have been producing a minimum of 650b.h.p. Assuming a figure of 15.75b.h.p. per 1000r.p.m. that equates to a peak power speed of 11,800r.p.m. Perhaps that should read 'around 12,300r.p.m.' to allow for a fall in brake thermal efficiency with increasing speed. Even that speed logically ought to stress a 350cc. cylinder less than 11,000r.p.m. stresses a 437.5cc (3500cc ÷ 8) capacity cylinder.

The V8 engine Cosworth produced for 1989 ran to over 12,000r.p.m. chasing 650b.h.p. and it would clearly have given the Honda turbo a real run for its money had it been available in 1988. So too would have the Ferrari V12 and the Renault V10, which were likewise confined to test programmes in 1988. Arguably FISA got its equivalency formula pretty much right for 1988. But would a new generation atmo engine have stopped the relentless march of the Honda-McLaren turbo? Undoubtedly, with a 40kg. lighter chassis and unrestricted fuel one could have taken a share of the glory, particularly one allied to a low line package. That was the successful Honda-McLaren recipe for 1989. But in 1988 it would have been a far less efficient winner. A far less elegant answer to the challenge of that memorable season.